COMPUTER LOGIC,
TESTING AND VERIFICATION

DIGITAL SYSTEM DESIGN SERIES

ARTHUR D. FRIEDMAN, Editor

The George Washington University

ARSENAULT and ROBERTS

Reliability & Maintainability of Electronic Systems

BREUER

Digital System Design Automation: Languages, Simulation and Data Base

BREUER and FRIEDMAN

Diagnosis & Reliable Design of Digital Systems

FRIEDMAN

Logical Design of Digital Systems

FRIEDMAN and MENON

Theory & Design of Switching Circuits

ROTH

Computer Logic, Testing and Verification

COMPUTER LOGIC, TESTING AND VERIFICATION

J. PAUL ROTH

IBM Thomas J. Watson Research Center

COMPUTER SCIENCE PRESS

Computer Science Press, Inc.
9125 Fall River Lane
Potomac, Maryland 20854

1   2   3   4   5   6   85   84   83   82   81   80

Library of Congress Cataloging in Publication Data

Roth, John Paul, 1922-
  Computer logic, testing, and verification.

  (Digital system design series)
  Includes bibliographies and index.
  1. Logic circuits.   2. Logic design.   I.   Title.
II.   Series.
TK7888.4.R67   621.3819′5835   79-27230
ISBN 0-914894-62-5

To Dorothy, Dana, Erich and Fatemeh

PREFACE

This book describes work of the author over a period of 24 years, together with a stream of IBM colleagues, toward developing a coherent mathematical calculus and practice for computer design. It includes work on logic design (especially PLAs), testing, logic verification, embedding (wiring), repairable logic and regular-algorithm verification, some of these notably testing - the D-algorithm - having achieved worldwide usage.

The book is largely self-contained. For understanding it requires only a modest amount of mathematics or computer science.

Background: The nature of logic design

As a preliminary to the main contents of this monograph on computer design we describe the method of construction of logic design as used in these chapters.

We begin with primitive logic functions and the devices realizing them. A logic primitive L is a function realized by a device having a number of arguments $a1,...,ar$ and a number of output values $b1,...,bs$. The function or device is represented conventionally as $(b1,...,bs)=L(a1,...,ar)$. Now in general the function/device will have no memory: i.e. the output $b1,...,bs$ is the same for repetitions of the same input argument values $a1,...,ar$. The values of the input variables $a1,...,ar$ and output variables $b1,...,bs$ are binary, although for purposes of design, testing and simulation, we shall employ 3- and 5-valued calculi for design and testing purposes (cf. Chapters 1, 3 and 7). In general the functions, both primitive and complex, are not defined for all input patterns: they may have DON'T-CARE conditions.

A typical logic primitive is the And function A of two input arguments a,b with output c defined as: $c = 1$ if $a=b=1$; otherwise, $c = 0$. The And-Invert AI, a common building block, with d,e inputs and f as output is defined as $f=0$ if $d=e=1$; $f=1$ otherwise. There are similar And and AI functions for more than two input arguments. Also defined is the Or and its negation Nor. Some devices realize two or more individual functions together, such as A- and AI-multiple-output functions. More complex functions and devices are obtained by the successive identification of input arguments of one with output values of others. Each device or circuit or function may be thought of mathematically as a node of a directed graph.

If the design has no feedback (memory) then the function so realized has no memory and it is a "combinational" circuit. Such a design will have primary input variables PI not fed by other nodes in the design and primary output variables PO. The design then defines a composite function from PIs to POs, which is always well-defined when there is no feedback. Chapters 4, 5 and 6 treat various aspects of designs with memory; if the logic has feedback, a "regular" method (Chapter 4) of design is employed to ensure that the behavior of the logic is determinate.

Summary

1. Logic Minimization. In Chapter 1 we treat a classical problem, in which the design has just two levels of logic. This method is of special interest in the design of the programmed logic arrays PLAs currently in heavy use in large-scale integration LSI technology. Efficient methods and a calculus are developed for the optimization of logic in two levels for many outputs, a solution to a long-standing problem. The results of programming the algorithms are illustrated for NASA and IBM problems.

Actually a calculus of cubical complexes is developed as a means for defining algorithms associated with 2-level minimization. This calculus is utilized for design purposes in Chapters 2 and 4 and generalized to a 5-valued "D-calculus" for purposes of test generation in Chapters 3 and 5, and to the so-called physical design problem of embedding in Chapter 7. In addition it forms the basis of a generalization to a language for design algorithms, "R-notation", in Chapters 1 and 4.

2. Acyclic Logic Design. Chapter 2 gives methods for acyclic logic design, i.e. designs which have no feedback.

First, logic primitives are defined using cubical notation for various primitives: And-Inverts AI, Exclusive-Ors Xor, and Inverts N. In general the primitives are without memory. Each primitive is associated with a "logic block", having an input line for each argument and an output line for each (usually one) binary output variable.

Next, the *composition* of primitives is discussed. Here from an ensemble of primitives, connections are made by successively identifying an input (line, argument) of one primitive with an output line of another. This interconnection is made, in this chapter, in such a way that in the resulting graph no feedback is introduced. In addition a representation of such a "logic design" is given in terms of a "singular cover", having a "local" cover in terms of the inputs and outputs for each primitive function. Fig. 2.3 gives such a representation for a 2-level And/Or circuit while Fig. 2.4 gives it for the Majority function, also 2-level logic. But in general it is concerned with multi-level representations. In Chapters 1, 2 and 3 the cover is always acyclic, but after Chapter 4, it is also used for designs with feedback, i.e. cyclic designs with memory. In Section 2.7 the $P*$ algorithm, which transforms multilevel circuits to two level designs is defined. This process is subsequently used as part of a "redesign" algorithm: taking an extant design, converting it to two levels by $P*$, using multiple-output factorization as described in Chapter 2, and performing a conversion to change the "abstract" logic from Ands, Ors and Inverts to the logic of some specified technology ready for implementation. $P*$ may also be thought of as a means for defining the function of an acyclic logic design.

In Section 2.8 is described a factorization algorithm enabling one, e.g. for economy, to go from a 2-level to a controlled multilevel logic design. Section 2.9 describes means to transform a multiple-level logic design into a technology implementation.

3. Acyclic Testing. In Chapter 3 the diagnosis of automata failures, a subject of great importance for the computer industry, is considered for the acyclic case. In manufacture as well as in the field, it is important to be able to detect failures. In LSI and very large-scale integration VLSI technologies, large pieces of the logic are packaged into assemblages: chips or modules or boards. Chapter 3 considers the acyclic case while Chapter 5 treats "regular" sequential testing. In general, stimulus to and response from individual circuits is not externally available directly. Therefore the behavior of the individual circuits is testable only through the medium of other circuits' inputs and outputs, usually in complex fashion. There might be on the order of 100 to 10000 circuits on a chip. Diagnosis consists of detecting failures inside the chip from the periphery. This introduces a new mathematical problem invented by the technology. A calculus of five values, plus the D-algorithm, is presented to generate tests to detect chip failures. In Section 3.5 an "optimized" version of the D-algorithm is given. In Section 3.10 the D-algorithm is extended to distinguish between two failures, a process fundamental to diagnosis.

In testing, one is given a set of failures and the goal is a set of tests T to detect each of these failures. The TESTDETECT algorithm is used in this connection. Given a test T, TESTDETECT ascertains all failures detected by *T*. It is an order of magnitude more efficient than simulation. It is given in Chapter 5 for the first time for regular sequential designs. The *D*-algorithm and TESTDETECT together are used by IBM and others to solve the testing problem.

4. Logic Automation. In Chapter 4 a variety of subjects relating to automatic design is discussed. First indeterminacy in logic designs, i.e., input sequences wherein the corresponding outputs are unpredictable, is treated.

The regular method of design, *R*-design, has the characteristic that it has no indeterminacies, an important characteristic of a design. Essentially an *R*-design is constructed systematically with a pair of registers, nonoverlapping in time, placed on every feedback loop. *R*-design was used for IBM System/360 Model 40, proving its cost feasibility, and for IBM System 370 Model 195, proving its speed feasibility. Its determinacy permits the extension of the *D*-algorithm to *R*-design (Chapter 5).

A notation for algorithms, the *R*-notation, is defined for specifying algorithms at a high level. Means to transform an *R*-algorithm to an *R*-design is exemplified. PL/R, a microscopic variant of PL/I restricted to logic operations, is developed as a specialization of the *R*-notation, and a compiler RTRAN, which transforms PL/R programs into regular logic designs (RLDs), *R*-designs, is described. Several examples are presented in detail.

In addition an inverse R* of RTRAN is described, which changes (low-level) RLDs into (high-level) PL/Rs. This program is used in dealing with engineering changes, keeping the PL/R and *R*-design levels consonant. It, together with RTRAN, can be used for automatic redesign.

In Section 4.11, three systems for computer design are described. One was used in IBM System/360, another in parts of subsequent machines.

5. Sequential Testing. Chapter 5 is concerned with testing for failures in cyclic logic designs, which in general is much more difficult than testing of loop-free logic. In its unaugmented form, a test for a failure in cyclic logic will consist of a *sequence* of input patterns, hence the name "sequential testing".

The "loop-cutter" method attempted to construct a test for an *arbitrarily* interconnected logical design. In this procedure certain special logic configurations of primitives constituted memory devices, called registers, and no means for identifying registers as such was used in the specifications. As a result they had to be reconstructed from the logic. Loops were cut in a systematic manner to yield an acyclic model. If one wanted a test of length n, then n copies were made and connected iteratively. Potential test sequences were computed and then checked for indeterminacies in the original model. More often than not they would be rejected by the (Eichelberger) simulator detecting indeterminacies. This method by and large was not effective for computing tests.

The second method (Section 5.2) was an adaptation of the D-algorithm to level sensitive scan design LSSD testing. The procedure developed by M. J. Y. Williams and Angell (1973) consists in adding to an R-design the ability to act as a shift register in the test mode for reading in and out test data. LSSD (Eichelberger and T.W. Williams 1977) is an extension of SCAN (Carter et al 1964) which was used in the design of among others IBM System/360 model 50. Because the feedback loops are effectively cut logically for test purposes by the LSSD latches, sequential diagnosis is reduced to combinational or acyclic diagnosis. This simplification makes LSSD a very effective tool.

The next section of Chapter 5 is devoted to test generation for regular logic designs. Here register pairs are inserted in the design of each feedback loop, with nonoverlapping clock pulses; these assure that test sequences are always valid. Yet the design is not rendered acyclic *a la* LSSD. Thus for test purposes it seems necessary to generate sequences of input patterns for tests for failures. In this regular design or R-design, only the feedback loops between registers are cut: the registers themselves are not cut. The primitives of the system consist in logic blocks and registers, which in general contain feedback. An iterative model is made of this cut system and tests are generated by means of the D-algorithm extended to include the local behavior of the registers. There must be sequences of D-cubes and singular cubes for their analysis.

Then a test sequence is generated for an iterated model, via the D-algorithm, extended, cf. Figs. 5.2 and 5.3. This test sequence is always determinate. It yields testing procedures, sequences instead of a single test, at some additional cost in computing time but without the need, as with LSSD, for the addition of hardware in the realization. This might be an important consideration, e.g. for microprocessors wherein additional hardware might not be tolerated.

Given a test sequence for a failure in a regular design, it is important to know of all failures detected by this same test sequence. This can be accomplished by a program TESTDETECT, described in Chapter 3 for the acyclic combinational case. It was experimentally demonstrated (Bouricius, et al 1969) as faster than simulation. Regular TESTDETECT is an extension to regular design.

Final sections discuss delay testing and short testing.

6. Logic Verification. Chapter 6 is concerned with hardware verification. For LSI and VLSI designs, it is particularly important that the design be correct *before* fabrication. Guaranteeing that a design is correct is of course an important characteristic for any algorithm whether realized as hardware or software. To verify a design we require another design for comparison. For hardware designs, however, we have an advantage in that we can have available two independent expressions for the design.

In our case we have first a high-level definition of the design, in PL/R or any, e.g., flowchart, language. Assume that the low-level implementation of the PL/R is performed manually, to form a design M. In order to verify M we first form an automatic implementation A using RTRAN. We then invoke an efficient procedure to verify M against A. This is done most expeditiously for acyclic, combinational logic or LSSD. VERIFY is a special case of the CONSISTENCY subroutine of the D-algorithm. It starts with a pair of corresponding outputs, in contrast to simulation procedures which start with input patterns. Opposite values are assigned to primary outputs and then a recursive march is made back to the primary inputs of the combined network to ascertain whether there are PI patterns consistent with the output assignment. If there are, then the designs M and A are inconsistent which would indicate that there is a mistake in M, the manual design, or inconceivably, that A, the automatic design, is at fault! If no counter-example is produced by VERIFY, the designs are equivalent.

For control logic, having relatively few levels of logic compared to arithmetic, running time for VERIFY has been quite manageable for LSSD designs in the order of many thousands of circuits when SEGMENT, a simplifying procedure, is used.

VERIFY is here extended to sequential regular designs. Of course test running time spirals in changing from acyclic to sequential verification-the price for less hardware in the end-product.

In Section 6.4 a method of defining an incomplete design (having DON'T-CAREs) is given; VERIFY is extended so that it is guaranteed to compute a CARE test distinguishing two designs, if one exists.

A large jump in speed can be obtained if the designs being compared are almost equivalent (special case, almost identical) and one takes advantage of this fact; this occurs when a design with engineering changes is compared to the original design: here one treats the two designs as one design, with a "failure"; this enables one to apply the D-algorithm with an enormous increase in efficiency (Section 6.6). The same giant increase in speed holds true when comparing R-algorithms (cf. 9. below).

Comparisons are made with other methods, notably the Boolean difference method.

7. Logic Embedding. Chapter 7 is a brief presentation of results for embedding a graph - here a logic design - onto a complex of 3-dimensional cells constituting the chip, a generalization from the cubical calculus of Chapter 1. It is the thesis that if all or some of the nodes of the graph are selected, then the interconnecting line segments must be defined one at a time, and in so doing it would be convenient to have a calculus to keep track of and manipulate the remaining unfilled spaces. A *cell calculus* is developed for purposes of these calculations. The #-product (pronounced "sharp-product") is a generalization of this notion. Experimental results justify this approach.

8. Repairable Logic. Chapter 8 describes the *universal function schema*, a method of design which allows the logic to realize any function up to a given size, as well as automatic detection, diagnosis and *repair* of failures. The price is an order of magnitude increase in size. This schema might have application for a technology, such as Josephson (1977), wherein the circuits are highly inaccessible. Fundamental is the notion of the general purpose spare.

9. R-algorithm Verification. The problem of algorithm verification is significant and difficult. In earlier chapters we used the R-notation in which to define algorithms called R-algorithms. In this chapter we extend the notation to incomplete algorithms and extend the techniques of RTRAN, VERIFY and the D-algorithm to the verification of R-algorithms: we transform, according to a compiler R, R-algorithms into an in general incomplete logic design; we then ascertain the equivalence between two R-algorithms by means of VERIFY or, in the case where they are almost equivalent (much faster) by the D-algorithm applied to their hardware realizations. The strictly finite character of regular algorithms makes it possible to verify them.

It is common to compare the behavior of an algorithm with an earlier version - say the last. In this case the hardware realizations under RTRAN may be considered, as above, as a single design, with failure the difference in their designs; thus the D-algorithm may be invoked to compute distinguishing tests, if they exist, with a substantial gain in speed. It is estimated that almost equivalent R-algorithms whose realizations do not exceed 50,000 circuits can be verified by the (modified) D-algorithm in acceptable computer time. The more difficult problem of program verification remains unsolved.

That this work may have significance beyond that of designing computers is indicated in the paper by R. D. Traub, M.D., and J. P. Roth, "Potential Significance to Neurophysiology of Design Algorithms for Digital Computers", *IBM J. of Research and Development*, vol. 21, (1977), pp. 572-575.

Acknowledgements

This book represents work largely by the author together with an extended number of colleagues including Eric G. Wagner, Harry Halliwell, Peter R. Schneider, Gianfranco R. Putzolu, W. C. Carter, Jerome Kurtzberg, R. M. Karp, R. E. Miller, Hamed Ellozy, W. G. Bouricius, J. H. Griesmer, Leroy Junker, all of IBM, and Marvin Perlman of CALTECH Jet Propulsion Laboratory. Valued was the programming of Harry Halliwell, P. R. Schneider, P. N. Sholtz, J. M. Galey, J. Sanborn, A. E. Randlev, Hamed Ellozy, B. Lewis, Leroy Junker, R. N. Norby and John B. Bendas.

An early version, 1973, of this material was given in a course, "Digital Computer Systems Design" (CE E6827), at Columbia University, Department of Electrical Engineering and Computer Science. Still earlier were my 1959 Italian lectures at the *Centro Internazionale Matematic Estivo* sponsored by the University of Rome. The material was also used in 1976 to prepare lectures for delivery at the invitation of M. Gabriele Saucier, at *l'ecole national superieure d'informatique et de mathematique appliquees de grenoble*, FRANCE. A very early version (1957) of this material was given by the author in a course in the Mathematics Department of Princeton University in conjunction with A. W. Tucker.

Each chapter contains problems and a bibliography and concludes with a summary of other relevant work. Thus the book is of potential use as a text in a course in computer logic design. References are given by date of publication and possibly author, listed in the bibliography for each chapter.

I thank Mrs. Marcia B. Bollard for her expert typing and formatting of this text for printing on the IBM Experimental Printer, and Sally F. Dennis for her painstaking editing and her very effective indexing program. I am grateful to Arthur D. Friedman, editor-in-chief of *Computer Science Press, Inc.*, for his comments and final editing of the text, and to Barbara Friedman, president, for her careful and helpful consideration during the birth of the book.

I wish to express my gratitude to IBM managers: G. Radin, D. P. Rozenberg, H. Schorr, C. V. Freiman, Gene Amdahl and J. J. Isole Jr., for their help along the way.

Finally I wish to thank my revered friend, Professor R. L. Wilder, University of Michigan and University of California, Santa Barbara, who taught me mathematics at the University of Michigan.

J. Paul Roth
January 1980

CONTENTS

1. Logic Minimization 1

Introduction
1.1   Cubical Calculus 1
1.2   Approximate Optimization: SHRINK 10
1.3   Absolute Optimization: The Extraction Algorithm 12
1.4   Extraction Algorithm, Multiple-output Case 23
1.5   Regular Algorithmic Notation, *R*-notation 27
1.6   Program Runs 29
1.7   Decreasing the Size of Associative Logic Arrays 31
1.8   Other Work 32
         Problems 33
         Bibliography 37

2. Acyclic Logic

Introduction 40
2.1   Logic Primitives 40
2.2   Logic Composition 42
2.3   Function of Acyclic Logic Design 44
2.4   Fan-in and Fan-out 45
2.5   Level 45
2.6   Segmentation 46
2.7   *P**: Many Levels to Two-levels 46
2.8   Factorization 51
2.9   Implementation for LSI Logic 54
2.10   Automatic Logic 56
2.11   Other Work 57
         Problems 57
         Bibliography 57

3. Acyclic Testing

Introduction 59
3.1   Need for Testing 59
3.2   *D*-notation 61
3.3   Test Generation. 64
3.4   The *D*-algorithm, by Example 65
3.5   Optimized *D*-algorithm. 70
3.6   TESTDETECT 70
3.7   *D*-algorithm Used with TESTDETECT 74
3.8   Validity of the *D*-algorithm. 74
3.9   Delay Testing 75
3.10   Distinguishing Failures 78
3.11   Description of Distinguishing Algorithm. 80
3.12   Other Work. 82
        Problems. 83
        Bibliography 84

4. Logic Automation

Introduction 87
4.1   Indeterminacy in Logic. 88
4.2   Function of Cyclic Designs. 89
4.3   Simulation of Cyclic Logic 90
4.4   Regular Logic Design. 91
4.5   LSSD 92
4.6.   Delay Calculation 93
4.7   Regular Notation 93
4.8   PL/R 96
4.9   RTRAN 98
4.10   R*, Inverse to RTRAN. 100
4.11   Systems for Computer Design. 102
4.12   Other Work. 105
        Problems. 105
        Bibliography 105

5. Sequential Testing

Introduction 108
5.1   Loop-cutter 109
5.2   LSSD Testing 112
5.3   Testing Regular Designs 128
5.4   Regular TESTDETECT 117
5.5   Delay Testing 120
5.6   Short Testing 121
5.7   Other Work 121
        Problems 123
        Bibliography 123

6. Logic Verification

Introduction 125
6.1   Acyclic Verificaton 126
6.2   Verification of LSSD Designs 128
6.3   Regular Verification 129
6.4   Verification Against Algorithmic Specifications 130
6.5   Consistency of Incomplete Designs 130
6.6   Consistency Between Almost Equivalent Designs 134
6.7   Other Work 137
        Problems 137
        Bibliography 138

7. Logic Embedding

Introduction 139
7.1   Cell Calculus 140
7.2   Interface 141
7.3   #-product 141
7.4   Embedding Algorithms 143
7.5   Other Work 144
        Problems 145
        Bibliography 146

8. Repairable Logic

Introduction 147
8.1   Universal Element 148
8.2   Two-level Universal Function Schemas 148
8.3   Functions Realized by UAs 149
8.4   Universal AI 150
8.5   Feedback 153
8.6   Other Work 155
        Problems 156
        Bibliography 156

9. R-algorithm Verification

Introduction 158
9.1 R-notation for Incomplete Regular Algorithms 159
9.2   Definition of Primitives 163
9.3   Hardware Compiler R of R-notation 167
9.4   Verification of R-algorithms 168
9.5   Other Work 169
        Problems 169
        Bibliography 170

Index 171

List of Figures

1.1   *3-cube* xxx and its faces 6
1.2   Logic geometry 7
1.3   Illustration of #-product 9
1.4   A cubical complex Z(1) 20
1.5   Z(1) with first-order extremals removed. 20
1.6   Z(2) with <-cubes removed 20
1.7   Z(2) with second-order extremals removed. 20
1.8   Third-order extremal 20
1.9   The prime cubes Z(1) (no extremals). 22
1.10   Complex Z(2) (*a* treated as extremal) 22
1.11   Complex with *LT*-cubes removed 22
1.12   Complex from which *a* has been removed 22
1.13   Complex in a 9-dimensional cube 24
1.14   MIN370 output for a binary adder 30
1.15   Frisiani's rendition of *5-cube*. 34

2.1   A logic block AI 41
2.2   Negate function. 42
2.3   And/Or circuit, functional expression and local cover. 43
2.4   Majority function. 44
2.5   4-bit PARITY 45
2.6   *P**-operation going from design in 3 levels to 2 47
2.7   Schneider's example - all blocks AIs 49
2.8   Factorization. 55

3.1   Primitive *D*-cube of failure of an AI 60
3.2   Computing test for failure in majority circuit 62
3.3   A circuit, its cover and primitive *D*-cubes for the
       D-algorithm. 66
3.4   Schneider's design 69
3.5   Design demonstrating need for a reconvergence
       condition 73
3.6   Output for TESTDETECT 76

3.7   TESTDETECT example 77

4.1   Register with races. 88
4.2   Indeterminate acyclic design 90
4.3   Babylonian square-root machine 95

5.1   Example of loop-cutter. 110
5.2a R-design T 114
5.2b   Cut-design T* 114
5.3   Iterated cut model T#. 115
5.4   1-bit register and its *pdcf*s and *pdc*s (partial list). 116
5.5   Second scheme 118
5.6   Sequential TESTDETECT, example. 119

6.1   VERIFY on a small example. 127
6.2   Verification of high-level specification against
       detailed logic. 131
6.3   Realization for incomplete specification 133
6.4   Implementation of second incomplete design 135
6.5   Verification of almost equivalent designs using
       the D-algorithm. 136

7.1   2-cell $<(0,0,0),(4,1,0)>$. 140
7.2   Geometric representation of cells, their
       interfaces, and their #-products. 142
7.3   Deduction of path from chain 144

8.1   Universal And UA, with r inputs. 150
8.2   UFS XOr 151
8.3   Universal AI, UAI 152
8.4   Multiple level universal circuit. 153
8.5   Universal regular module handling feedback 154

9.1   Example of box-node for output variable v of a
       cell-cover 160
9.2   Iterated hardware realization of Babylonian
       R-algorithm. 162

Chapter 1

LOGIC MINIMIZATION

Introduction. An arbitrary function of r binary inputs and s binary outputs is described in cubical notation. The function corresponds to a realization in two levels of logic of the so-called programmed logic array, PLA (1975, Fleisher and Maissel; 1979, Weinberger), which is an important tool in large scale integration, LSI. The problem of an optimum realization is defined and both approximate (SHRINK) and exact (EXTRACTION) algorithms are given for this, in general, multiple-output problem.

A calculus of cubical complexes is defined. The calculus is first generalized in the R-notation for algorithm specification; then in later chapters in the D-algorithm for failure diagnosis; then, as a cellular calculus for physical design, precisely, for the "embedding" problem. Geometric interpretations are given for the single-output problem. Commercial examples are given of runs of a computer program of the algorithms.

1.1 Cubical Calculus.

Singular Cubes. Let F be a function of r inputs (arguments) and s outputs (values). Inputs and outputs are binary. In general not every output is defined for all input combinations. Input/output combinations for which the function is undefined are called DON'T-CARE conditions; those that are, CARE conditions.

Perhaps the first use of this cubical calculus (see below), was by Shannon, 1938, for *relay* circuits, although Boole's work, 1852, on "Boolean Algebra" was more distant in time. (See Miller, 1965.) Actually PLAs are logically slightly more complicated: e.g., the "fan-in" (the number of lines entering a block) of the Ands is restricted. Let the inputs and outputs of F be labelled $a1,...,ar$ and $b1,...,bs$. Then a *singular cube* is an assignment $a1=u1,...,ar=ur$; $b1=v1,...,bs=vs$ of values $u1,...,ur$ and $v1,...,vs$ equal to 0,1,x to each of the variables labelled $a1,...,ar$, and $b1,...,bs$. A singular cube is written $u \mid v$ where $u = u1,...,ur$ and $v = v1,...,vs$. Here the symbol $\mid$ (pronounced "slash"), is used to denote simple separation of input- and output-variables. (Later in a programming context, quite disjoint, it denotes the logical Or.) The u is called the *input part* and corresponds with *values* assigned the inputs of F. The v is termed the *output part* and corresponds with *values* assigned the outputs of F. The assignment of x as the value of an input or output variable means that the value of this variable is unspecified.

If a,b,c are input variables and d,e,f output variables then $01x \mid 10x$ would mean: when $a=0$ and $b=1$, regardless of the value of c, then d would assume the value 1, e the value 0, with no specification for f.

A singular cube thus defines a correspondence between values assigned input variables and values assigned to output variables; it constitutes a definition of a function. The term "singular" indicates that there is a relation between input- and output-parts.

We shall impose a condition of *consistency* on a *set* of singular cubes such that they unambiguously define a function.

Vertex. A *vertex* is a special singular cube in which all coordinates for the input part are 0 or 1 and all but one of the output part are x. This means that all the input coordinates are specified and only one of the outputs. A vertex refers then to just one output. In a cube, coordinates 0 and 1 are referred to as *bound* coordinates; x, as *free*.

Contain. A singular cube $a \mid b$ is said to *contain* vertex $v \mid w$ if $v \mid w$ can be obtained from $a \mid b$ by appropriately changing all xs in the input part of $a \mid$ b to 1s or 0s and by changing all bound output coordinates, save one, to x. If singular cube $a \mid b$ contains vertex $v \mid w$, then $a \mid b$ contains all the information of $v \mid w$, in the definition of a function. For example, $10x \mid 11$ contains both vertices $101 \mid 1x$ and $100 \mid x1$.

Face.   If singular cube $a \mid b$ contains all the vertices of singular cube $c \mid d$, we say then that $a \mid b$ *contains* $c \mid d$ and that $c \mid d$ is a *face* of $a \mid b$. Alternatively, $c \mid d$ is a face of $a \mid b$ and $a \mid b$ *contains* $c \mid d$ if $c \mid d$ may be transformed into $a \mid b$ by an appropriate change of free input coordinates into bound coordinates and an appropriate change of bound output coordinates into free.   For example $x0x \mid 11$ contains $10x \mid 1x$ and $x1x1 \mid 1x1$ contains $11x1 \mid 1x1$ and $x1x1 \mid xx1$. An *output face* of a cube u is obtained by changing one or more of its bound output coordinates to an x.   An *input face* is obtained by changing a free input coordinate to a 1 or 0.   Thus $x0x \mid 1x$ is an output face and $10x \mid 11$ is an input face of $x0x \mid 11$.

Henceforth we shall abbreviate the term singular cube by the term *cube* alone.

Interface.   The *interface* (or *intersection*) of cubes $a \mid b$ and $c \mid d$ is defined as the smallest cube containing all of their common vertices - it is contained in all cubes containing them.   If they have no common vertices, they are said to be *disjoint*.   Now we give an analytic definition.   First we define the interface of single coordinates, using the symbol I for interface, $0I0=0Ix=xI0=0$; $1I1=1Ix=xI1=1$; $xIx=x$; $1I0=0I1=q$; here the symbol q denotes conflict.   Then the *interface* of two cubes is the cube formed from their individual coordinate interfaces.

Cubes are said to be *consistent* if a conflict q in the output parts of their interface implies similarly a disagreement q in their input parts. For cubes to define a function they *must* be consistent.   This condition insures that common input parts of different cubes defining a function may not have conflicting outputs: if their output parts are disjoint then so are their inputs.

For instance, the cubes $1x1 \mid 1x$ and $01x \mid x1$ have the interface $q11 \mid 11$ and are therefore consistent.   The cubes $x00x \mid 1x1$ and $xx01 \mid 01x$, having interface $x001 \mid q11$, are inconsistent.   Cubes $1x1 \mid 0x1$ and $01x \mid 11x$ having interface $q11 \mid q11$ are consistent.   An interface having a coordinate equal to q is said to be a *degenerate* cube. Otherwise, *nondegenerate*.   Two cubes are *disjoint* if their interface is degenerate.   If they are consistent it is sufficient that the input part of their interface is degenerate.   By the same definition we may also say that input parts are disjoint.   That cubes a and b are disjoint may be denoted ϕ, for "empty cube", $aIb = \phi$.

Cover and Function. A set of pairwise consistent, nondegenerate cubes, all referring to the same input and output variables, is termed a *cover*. A cover C defines a function $F=F(C)$; F is defined for each vertex v contained in each cube of C, and only those. By grace of their mutual consistency, cubes of C containing the same vertex v assign the same value.

Interface of covers. The notion of interface may be extended. Let C be a cover and e a cube. Then the *interface e I C* may be defined as the set of interfaces e I c, for each c in C. The interface of a cube e and a cover C determines the vertices that e has in common with C. e I C is itself a cover. It is similarly extended to the intersection of two covers. Let C and D be compatible covers, i.e., having the same input- and output-variables. Then the interface C I D consists of the set of interfaces c I d where c belongs to C and d belongs to D. In general we will not include degenerate cubes in lists of interfaces. The interface C I D is itself a cover of the vertices belonging to both C and D.

Vertex. Vertices contained in some cube of a cover are CARE conditions or CAREs of the cover and the function so defined. Those that are not, are DON'T-CARE *conditions* or DON'T-CAREs.

We shall be continuously concerned with enlarging cubes of a cover thereby reducing their "cost". Thus we define coface, a natural notion, a term depending not just upon a cube but the cover which contains it as well.

Coface. Given a cube c of a cover C, we say that cube e is a *coface* of c, with respect to C, if c is a face of e (e contains c) *and* e itself is consistent with the cubes of C.

One way to obtain a coface of a cube c of a cover C is to change a bound input coordinate of c to an x or to change a free output coordinate to a bound one (1 or 0), possibly in several places; in addition it is necessary to interface this newly formed cube with each (other) cube of C to ensure that it and C are consistent.

In the formation of cofaces of the cubes of a cover, we shall allow inconsistencies among the cofaces but each must be consistent with the cubes of the initial cover. (Cf. SHRINK, defined later in this chapter).

In order to formulate our 2-level multiple-output minimization problem in satisfactory mathematical fashion, we introduce the notion of a cubical complex.

Cubical Complex. Let C be a cover. A *cubical complex K(C)* of C is formed from C by adjoining to C according to the following rule: if c is a cube of K then its faces and cofaces, with respect to C, also belong to K. This is an enormous simplification of original (1955, Roth) and subsequent definitions. A cube z of complex K is *prime* if it is not the face of any other cube of K (*prime implicant* for one output and no DON'T-CAREs).

As an example of a complex consider the function AI defined by the cover $C = 111\,|\,0;\ 0xx\,|\,1;\ x0x\,|\,1;\ xx0\,|\,1$; none of these cubes have cofaces; there are nine 1-dimensional (one x) faces and eight vertices.

Consider the cover defined by $C = 11\,|\,0;\ 00\,|\,1$; this has DON'T-CARE conditions covered by $01\,|\,x$ and $10\,|\,x$. The cubical complex $K(C)$ contains in addition to C the cofaces $x1\,|\,0;\ 1x\,|\,0;\ x0\,|\,1;\ 0x\,|\,1$; these conflict with each other but not with the initial cover. Figure 1.1 depicts the 3-cube xxx (implying just one output).

Let C be a cover defining a cubical complex K. A subset M of K is said to form a *cover of C* if M covers each vertex of C, i.e. each vertex of C is contained in some cube of M.

There is a simple geometrical visualization of cubical complexes and functions with one output, which we illustrate here for functions of three input variables. (See e.g. Figure 1.4 for a high-dimensional case (about 12)). We sketch this for a simple problem. In Figure 1.1 is a 3-dimensional cube, within which such functions can be represented. Vertices of the function are identified with vertices of the cube.

It may be helpful to consider a geometric representation of a cubical complex, a 3-input 1-output function. The same kind of representation, same notation, holds for higher input dimensions. (I know of no neat representation of multiple-output problems.) In Figure 1.2a is represented, in skeletal geometric fashion, the vertices of a cover defining a function and cubical complex: only those with output 1 are shown, with slash and output coordinate deleted. (We suspend specification as to which of the remaining vertices assume value 0 or are DON'T-CAREs.) We call Figure 1.2a the *0-skeleton*. Vertices 000 and 100 have been placed contiguously, corresponding to the fact that they differ in *exactly* one coordinate. Similarly with the pairs (000,001) (100,101) (001,101) and (001,011). Each such pairing entrains certain simplifications of the cover representing the function and thus in its *implementation* depending upon the technology (from relays to LSI transistors).

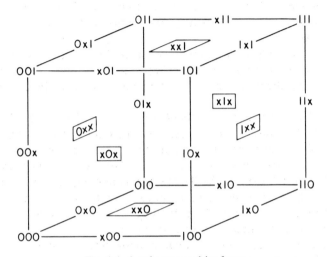

Fig. 1.1 *3-cube* xxx and its faces

Note that the pair of 0-cubes (this means cubes of degree 0 rather than cubes with output 0) 000, 100 define the 1-cube x00; x00 *covers* the same vertices that this pair does but it is less costly both in terms of the number of cubes - one instead of two as well as in the number of bound values - two instead of six.

Figure 1.2b is a representation of all the five 1-cubes (indicated by the solid lines) so formed: the *1-skeleton*. Note that we could obtain a cover of the five vertices with three 1-cubes.

Exercise. Find two covers each containing three 1-cubes from Figure 1.2b.

We see further that 1-cubes x00 and x01 differ in just one coordinate. (Similarly 00x and 10x.) These two determine the 2-cube x0x, which has them as well as vertices 000, 100, 101, 001 as *faces:* x0x covers them all. Similarly for the opposites 00x, 10x. Therefore x0x can be substituted for either (or both) such pairs in any cover. Thus

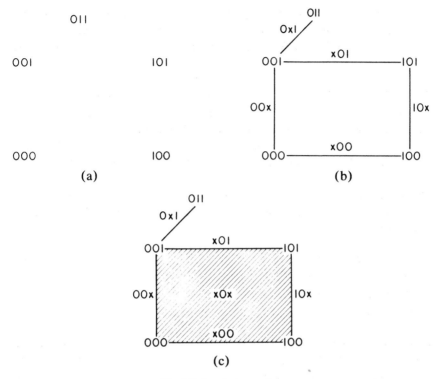

Fig. 1.2 Logic geometry

from the 2-skeleton (Figure 1.2c) we deduce the (minimum!) cover x0x, 0x1.

The vertices 000, 101, 001, 011, which constitute a cover *C* or say covers 0x1, x00, x01 or 0x1, 10x or x0x, 0x1 all define cubical complex *K(C)* consisting of the cubes x0x, x00, x01, 00x, 10x, 0x1, 000, 100, 101, 001, 011. Note: x0x is a coface of x01, x00, ...000 but not 011, etc., and conversely 000,...,101 are faces of x0x, etc.

Exercise. Adjoin 010 as a DON'T-CARE. Draw figures corresponding to Figure 1.2. Render vertices 000, 100, 101, 001, 011 as 000 | 1, 100 | 1, 101 | 1, 001 | 1, 011 | 1 and 010 as 010 | x.

The *cubical complex K*, defined by any of these covers is composed from all the skeleta described plus the face- and coface-relations between them.

The cubical complex in (*r,s*)-dimensions, *r* inputs, *s* outputs, is a generalization of the Karnaugh map (1953) and the Veitch chart (1952), which are limited to (4,1)-dimensions.

A binary valued function partitions the vertices of the 3-cube xxx into two parts: those mapped into 1 and those into 0. In general there may also be DON'T-CARE conditions, those for which the function is not defined.

Cost. The *cost of a cube* v is any integer-valued function $p(v)$ such that if cube v contains cube w, then $p(v)$ is less than or equal to $p(w)$. The *cost of a cover* C is the sum of the costs of the cubes comprising it. (A larger cube v tends to cost less than a smaller cube w because v *covers* more than w does and its hardware realization in general costs less.)

The optimization problem we consider is: given a complex K defined by some cover C, and cost-function p, find a cover M of minimum cost, with respect to p.

CONTAIN Operation. Let C be a cover; the operation CONTAIN consists in deleting from C all cubes which are faces of other cubes of C. Clearly the result C' of applying CONTAIN to C covers precisely what C does.

#-product (pronounced "sharp-product"). For this purpose we define a useful kind of differencing product, termed the #-product $a\#b$ of cube a with cube b; $a\#b$ consists of a cover of all vertices of a which are *not* contained in b, the cover composed from these vertices.
It is convenient to introduce first the #-product for cubes having just one output. There is no loss in generality in assuming that both output coordinates have the value 1. Let the cubes then be denoted $a\,|\,1$ and $b\,|\,1$ and let it be assumed that we are generating

$$(a\,|\,1)\#(b\,|\,1).$$

There are three rules.

Rule 1. If a and b are disjoint; then $(a\,|\,1)\#(b\,|\,1)=(a\,|\,1)$.

Rule 2. If a is contained in b, then $(a\,|\,1)\#(b\,|\,1)$ contains no cubes.

Rule 3. If neither conditions for Rules 1 and 2 hold, then the output will be a cover of certain faces of $a\,|\,1$ that are not in $b\,|\,1$. For each coordinate i for which $a(i)=x$ and $b(i)=e=1$ or 0, there will be a cube f in the #-product having $f(i)=e$ and all other $f(i) = \bar{e}$ and all other coordinates identical to those of a. (A bar above a variable, as $\bar{c}$, denotes the negation of this variable.) For example,

$$(1x1x\,|\,1)\#(x1x0\,|\,1) = 101x\,|\,1, \; 1x11\,|\,1;$$

similarly $(xxx\,|\,1)\#(101\,|\,1) = 0xx\,|\,1, \; x1x\,|\,1, \; xx0\,|\,1$, as illustrated in Figure 1.3. As can be seen from the illustration, the #-product is a geometric differencing operation.

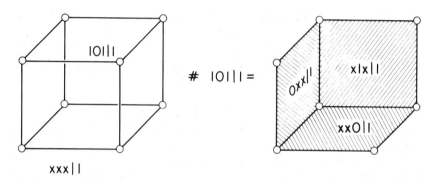

Fig. 1.3. Illustration of #-product

The rules of formation of the #-product are more complicated for the case of *multiple-output cubes*. The rules are stated only for nondegenerate cubes. Let $a\,|\,b$ and $c\,|\,d$ be cubes.

Rule 1. If $a\,|\,b$ and $c\,|\,d$ are *disjoint*, then $(a\,|\,b)\#(c\,|\,d)=a\,|\,b$.

Rule 2. If a is contained in c, then $(a\,|\,b)\#(c\,|\,d)=(a\,|\,e)$, where for all coordinates i for which $b(i)=d(i)$, $e(i)=x$; for those for which $b(i)=1$ (or 0) and $d(i)=x$, then $e(i)=b(i)$; if $b(i)=x$ then $e(i)=x$.

Rule 3. If neither conditions for Rules 1 and 2 hold, then the output will be a cover of faces of $a\,|\,b$, the cover composed from vertices of $a\,|\,b$ *not* in $c\,|\,d$. In $(a\,|\,b)\#(c\,|\,d)$ there first will be a single cube $a\,|\,f$, wherein all coordinates of f are x except those coordinates i where $b(i)=1$ (or 0) and $d(i)=x$. For these coordinates, $f(i)=b(i)$. Finally for each coordinate i for which $a(i)=x$ and $c(i)=e=1$ or 0, there will be a cube g in the #-product having $g(i) = \bar{e}$, with all other coordinates identical to those of $a \mid b$.

Consider a simple example: $a \mid b = 101 \mid 1x1$ and $c \mid d = xx1 \mid 11x$. These cubes are not disjoint so that Rule 1 does not apply. But on the other hand a is contained in c so that Rule 2 applies so that $(a \mid b)\#(c \mid d)=101 \mid xx1$. As another example,

$$(x0x \mid 1x1)\#(0x1 \mid x11)=x0x \mid 1xx, 10x \mid 1x1, x00 \mid 1x1.$$

c#C. The definition of #-product will be extended to the #-product of a cube with a cover. Let c be a cube and C a cover, $C=c1,c2,...,cn$. Then the *#-product* $c\#C$ is defined by the iterated formula $c\#C = ...((c\#c1)\#c2)...\#cn)$. At each stage CONTAIN is performed. The #-product $c\#C$ deletes from c all vertices of cubes of C.

#-Product $C\#D$ *of covers.* The #-product can likewise be extended to that between covers. If C and D are compatible (same input- and output-variables) covers then the #-product $C\#D$ is the set of all cubes $c\#D$ where c is a cube of C. For efficiency at *each* stage of $C\#D$ the CONTAIN Operation is performed, resulting in an enormous increase in speed.

We now describe an approximate algorithm called SHRINK for a solution of the optimization problem stated above.

1.2 Approximate Optimization: SHRINK. Let K be a complex defined by a cover C. Recall that a cube of K is *prime* if it is not contained in any other cube of K. In SHRINK a new cover M (for Minimum) will be constructed covering all the vertices of C and composed solely of prime cubes.

Redundancy. A cube r of cover E is said to be *redundant* if all of its CARE vertices are contained in other members of E. Otherwise it is *nonredundant.*

Proposition. Cube r of cover E is redundant if and only if

$$(r\#(E-r)) \quad I \quad C \qquad (I \text{ for interface})$$

is empty, where: C is a cover of the CARE conditions; $r\#(E-r)$ denotes the (iterated) #-product of each element of the cover $E-r$ from

r; the interface $(r\#(E-r))$ I C denotes the interface of each member of $(r\#(E-r))$ with each member of C.

We now describe this algorithm SHRINK for an approximate solution of the optimization problem stated above.

SHRINK. A new cover M will be constructed covering all the vertices of some cover C and composed solely of "nonredundant" (see below) prime cubes.

The steps to SHRINK are as follows:

Step 1. Perform CONTAIN on C, calling the result C', and select a cube c of cover C'.

Step 2. Form cofaces of c to produce prime cube z, in general by repeated cofacing. After each cofacing perform CON-TAIN on the cover so produced.

Step 3. Replace c in C' by z, to form $C*$.

Step 4. Remove from $C*$ all cubes contained in z to form $C\#$.

Step 5. Perform steps 1 through 4 for all cubes of $C\#$, to form cover P of prime cubes.

Step 6. Remove, in some order, from P all redundant cubes, to form nonredundant prime cover M.

The coface operation of Step 2 may be performed in different ways. Assume for purposes of exposition but with no loss of generality that the cover has an "ON-cover" CON, a cover for which all outputs are 1 or x and an "OFF-cover" $COFF$, a cover of all conditions for which each output is 0 or x. Then we attempt to coface c by changing a bound input coordinate of c to an x. We ascertain whether or not this is a correct coface by interfacing this with $COFF$. It is a correct coface if it does not have an interface with $COFF$. Likewise each output coordinate equal to x is changed to 1 and then checked to ensure that the expanded cube is consistent with C. For utility the SHRINK optimization is performed only for the ON-cover (or OFF-cover).

Example. We shall illustrate SHRINK with a single-output example. Initially the ON-cover consists of three cubes, while the OFF-cover consists of two. We shall first attempt to optimize the ON-cover only.

$$
\begin{array}{lll}
a & & 1x11 \mid 1 \\
b & & xx00 \mid 1 \\
c & & 11xx \mid 1 \\
\\
d & & x010 \mid 0 \\
e & & 0011 \mid 0 \\
\end{array}
$$

The first step CONTAIN is here vacuous. The next step is the cofacing operation. We start by lexicographic order with cube a. Here xx11 | 1 is not a valid coface since it interfaces the OFF-cube e. On the other hand 1xx1 | 1 is a valid coface and, since no further cofacing is possible, is prime.

Cube b has as prime coface the cube xx0x | 1, disjoint from d and e, (xxx0 | 1 is not a coface, interfacing, as it does, d.)

Finally c has as prime coface x1xx | 1. No CONTAIN operation is possible nor redundancy removal and we are left with the prime cube cover produced by SHRINK.

$$
\begin{array}{l}
1xx1 \mid 1 \\
xx0x \mid 1 \\
x1xx \mid 1 \\
\end{array}
$$

with again the OFF-array

$$
\begin{array}{l}
x010 \mid 0 \\
0011 \mid 0 \\
\end{array}
$$

1.3.   Absolute Optimization: The Extraction Algorithm. The algorithm given in the previous section is not guaranteed to yield a minimum solution, although it is quite fast and demands little storage. The procedure given in this section, the extraction algorithm, is, however, guaranteed to obtain a minimum, to the stated problem. It requires in general more time and more storage, on large problems, enormously more. There are chip designs, however, whose production or usage is sufficient to justify the extra running time, as we shall see subsequently. See also 1978 Roth. (Cf. problems for NASA, below.)

We first outline the extraction algorithm for the *single-output case.* Then we modify it to make it applicable to the multiple-output case.

A cube z of a complex K was defined as *prime* if it is not the face of any other cube of K.

Proposition. Let Z denote the set of all prime cubes of a single-output complex K. Then a minimum cover can be formed from Z alone.

Proof. Let c be a member of a cover C of K which is not prime. Let p be a prime cube containing c. Since c is not prime there will always be such p. By assumption on the cost function, the cost of p will not exceed the cost of c. Furthermore p will cover all the vertices which c covers. Thus the cover obtained by substituting p for c in C will cover all the CARE vertices of K and its cost will be no more. Q.E.D.

Therefore in constructing a minimum for single-output functions we can restrict ourselves only to prime cubes. Hence there is use for the following construction.

#-algorithm. We deal first with the case of a single output. Assume that the function F scheduled for implementation is given by a cover C. Assume with no loss of generality that C is split into a cover CON of the ON-vertices, the vertices assigned the value 1 by the function F defined by the cover, and a cover $COFF$ of the OFF-vertices, those assigned the value 0 by F.

We make an iterated use of the #-product to produce Z. The process is called the #-*algorithm*. Because of our single-output assumption we shall likewise be using the #-product in the single-output mode.

By construction Z will automatically be based on the ON-vertices, those assigned 1 by F, plus the DON'T-CARE vertices, those assigned no value by F. In general the solution will take *advantage* of the DON'T-CARE conditions. The construction starts with the OFF-cover $COFF$.

The construction uses what we call the *universal cube* Q whose input part, for a function of r input variables and one output variable, consists of r xs, each input variable having value x, and the one output variable having value 1 : $Q = xx...x \mid 1$.

Step 1. Change the output coordinate of each cube of the cover $COFF$ of the OFF-vertices of F from a 0 to a 1. Call the resulting cover $DOFF$.

Step 2. Form $Q\#DOFF$, performing at each stage the CONTAIN operation. Call the result Z.

Exercise. Prove that Z, formed by the above construction, consists of the set of all prime cubes of K, the space of the ON-vertices and the DON'T-CARE vertices of the function F.

If the cover $COFF$ of the OFF-conditions is not available but just a cover E of the ON- and DON'T-CARE-conditions then Z can be obtained by the *double #-procedure* $Q\#(Q\#E)$.

Disjoint #, #j. There is another form of the #-product which aids considerably in counting the number of vertices of a complex. (It was developed by Leroy Junker (1978) of the IBM T. J. Watson Research Center.) When the so-called "disjoint #", called $\#j$, is formed between cubes a and b, $a\#b$, it obtains a cover of disjoint cubes. Thus to compute the number of vertices in this cover it is only necessary to compute for each cube in the cover its dimension c, to raise to the cth power, $2^{**}c$, and sum over each cube. This technique has been used for statistical counting problems. (1976).

It also substantially reduces running time of the #-algorithm (cf. below). The only disadvantage of the disjoint # is that it does not in general produce prime cubes and therefore in the #-algorithm can be used only for the first stage of the process.

Let us first take an example. Consider the ordinary #-product and the disjoint #j-product of xxxx and 1011.

	xxxx		xxxx
#	1011	#j	1011
	0xxx		0xxx
	x1xx		11xx
	xx0x		100x
	xxx0		1010

It will be observed in the disjoint (Junker) sharp that each cube is rendered disjoint from its predecessors by disagreeing with each in successive coordinates. For example 100x is disjoint from 0xxx and 11xx in coordinates one and two respectively. Similarly 1010 differs from each of its three predecessors. Observe further that each cube of $\#j$ is a unique face of a corresponding cube of #.

This gives a key to their formation: To effect $a\#jb$, where a and b are cubes, form the ordinary $a\#b$; let the first cube c produced be as with the #-product; modify the second cube so that in the first coordinate $i(1)$ where c has a 1 (or 0) and d has an x, change this x to an opposite 0 (or 1) in the #*j*-product; for the third cube *e* produced by the #-product, make *e*'s *i*(1)-coordinate similarly equal to 0 (or 1); likewise find the second coordinate *i*(2) where *d* has a 1 (or 0) and *e* has an x; change this x to a 0 (or 1), rendering it thus disjoint from *c* and *d*. (Cf. 1978 Junker, Roth.)

Exercise. Perform an induction to define #*j* on coordinates *i*(1), *i*(2), etc. as defined above.

Example of #-algorithm. We shall take the example previously considered where the OFF-cover consists of the two cubes x010 and 0011 with the output coordinate deleted for simplicity. Accordingly Q=xxxx and the first step is the #-product xxxx#x010=x1xx, xx0x, xxx1; the next step is to sharp away 0011: (x1xx, xx0x, xxx1)#0011 = x1xx, xx0x, 1xx1, x1x1, xx01; After performing CONTAIN this reduces to

$$x1xx$$
$$xx0x$$
$$1xx1$$

which happens to be the same cover as obtained by SHRINK, although in general this is not the end of the extraction algorithm.

Extremal. An *extremal* is a prime cube which covers a CARE vertex that no other prime cube covers.

An extremal geometrically represents an "extreme" portion of the cubical complex. The next step is the computation of the extremals. It will be recalled that given a complex K of cubes, defined by an ON-cover and the DON'T-CARE conditions, the #-algorithm was employed to produce the set Z of prime cubes. To obtain a minimum, it is sufficient to restrict attention to the prime cubes.

Example. Figure 1.4 depicts (cf. 1958 Roth) a cubical complex, in some high number of dimensions. The prime cubes are labelled *a* through *t*; there are no initial DON'T-CARE conditions. The extremals consist of the cubes *a,d,q,t*. As will be observed the extremals consist of the "extreme" cubes; hence the name.

Let us remember that we are dealing at this point with the single-output case. The significance of extremals is given in the next proposition.

Proposition. Let K be a complex. Suppose that the cost function is such that the cost of a proper face (i.e. not the cube itself) of a cube is greater than that of a cube itself. Then a minimum cover M must contain each extremal.

Proof. By definition an extremal e covers a vertex which no other prime cube does. If e is not in M then a face of e must be. By definition of the cost function, this will cost more than e. Hence M is not a minimum. Contradiction. Q.E.D.

In the case where the cost of a cube equals the cost of a face, then a face in a minimum cover may be substituted for an extremal in a cover. Still the cost is not (by the definition of cost) increased by substituting an extremal for its face. Next a means will be described for computing the extremals of K.

Proposition. Assume that CON is a cover of the ON-vertices, the CARE vertices assigned the value 1 by the function F defined by the cover. Similarly let $COFF$ denote a cover of the OFF-vertices, those assigned the value 0 by F. Let Z be the prime cubes of CON plus the DON'T-CARE conditions. Then e, a member of Z is an extremal if and only if $(e\#(Z-e))$ I CON is not empty. (I denotes interface.)

Let $E1$ denote the set of (first-order) extremals. By the previous Proposition, $E1$ will be part of our minimum cover. Let $M1=E1$ denote this partial minimum cover. Accordingly we shall reduce the CARE conditions CON by $E1$: Let $C2=CON\#E1$. Then $C2$ contains all of the CARE conditions that are not yet covered by $M1$.
We are now in a position to introduce the LESS-THAN operation to introduce further simplifications.

LESS-THAN $<$. Given a cover C of the CARE conditions, we say that cube u is LESS-THAN cube v (denoted by $u<v$) if 1) the cost of u is less than or equal to v; and 2) u I C is contained in v.

Proposition. Let V be a cover containing the CARE conditions C of a complex K. Let v be an element of V and let w be another cube of K, with $v<w$. Then $(V-v)\cup w$, is another cover of C, of no greater cost, where $\cup$ stands for union.

Let LT denote the LESS-THAN operation consisting of deleting from a cover all cubes LESS-THAN others in the cover. Let $P2 = Z\text{-}E1$, the truncated list of prime cubes.

Proposition. A minimum cover of $C2$, the portion of CON not covered by the first-order extremals $E1$, may be obtained as a subset of $Z2$, the subset of $P2$ maximal under LT.

In view of this proposition, LT will consist in deleting all nonmaximal cubes from $P2$, prime cubes without extremals, to form $Z2$, the subset of $P2$ maximal under $<$, as determined by LT. In general, LT "uncovers" new extremals.

Crown. One of the operations which is often performed in the extraction algorithm is LT. Thus any speedup of LT has substantial positive effects on the performance of the extraction algorithm. Robert Ritz (1958), supplied the notion of "crown" to effect such a speedup.

The formation of the *crown* cr is accomplished by a kind of coordinate product cri, a product formed for each coordinate i. The coordinate rules are: if in any coordinate i for a number of cubes there is a disagreement among the differing coordinates, then $cri = x$; if all the values for a given coordinate have the same value v, then $cri = v$. Then the crown cube cr of the cover of cubes is

$$cr = cr1, cr2, ..., crk;$$

where k is the number of coordinates for each cube.

Thus the following cover C of cubes 1x11, 10x1, 11xx; has the crown $cr(C) = 1\text{xxx}$.

Theorem. A cube z contains all the cubes in a cover C if and only if z contains the crown of C.

Exercise. Prove the above theorem.

Recursion. From this point the extraction algorithm goes into a recursive mode. The above operations are repeated. Reviewing, we have: a set of CARE conditions $C2 = C1\#E1$, where $C1 = CON$; a new reduced set of prime cubes $Z2$ equal to $Z1 = Z$ reduced by the extremals $E1$ and by the LT operation applied to the remainder. A partial minimum cover $M1$, is defined as $E1$; we then compute a set of second-order extremals $E2$ according to a formula similar to that above: e is a *second-order extremal* if and only if

$$e\#(Z2-e) \ I \ C2 \neq \phi,$$

where ϕ denotes the empty set.

Then the remaining CARE conditions are defined as the cover $C3 = C2\#E2$; the new partial solution is $M2 = M1 \cup E2$.

The new reduced prime cube collection is defined as $P3 = Z2 - E2$. We again perform the operation LT, removing nonmaximal cubes to form a new set $Z3$, contained in $P3$, of prime cubes on which to compute the third-order extremals, etc.

The process terminates either when the CARE conditions $C(i) = C(i-1)\#E(i-1)$ reduce to the empty set or else when $E(i)$ becomes empty, i.e., when no new extremals are uncovered. In the first case $M(i) = M(i-1) \cup E(i)$ is a minimum. In the latter case the BRANCHING mode is entered. Here essentially two conditional solutions are computed, the exact solution being one of them.

Branching. The process goes as follows. Suppose we are at the ith stage with the partial solution $M(i)$, not a complete solution:

$$CON\#M(i) \neq \phi$$

Suppose further (the branching hypothesis) that in the ith stage no new extremals are uncovered:

$$E(i) = \phi.$$

Then, by some heuristic procedure, select a (prime) cube e' in $Z(i)$. We construct two constrained solutions. In the first we treat e' as if it were an extremal and form

$$M(i+1) = M(i) \cup e'$$

and go on , in the LESS-THAN, etc. operations to form a minimum cover $M(e')$ subject to the constraint that it contain e'. In this process, possibly several levels of additional branching may be necessary. (In MIN370, a PL/I program of the multiple-output extraction algorithm, 50 levels of branching are allowed. See below).

On the other hand, in the second constrained solution the prime cube e' selected is treated as if it were less than some other cube of $Z(i)$ and so is discarded. In this construction

$$P(i+1) = Z(i)\text{-}e'$$

and a minimum cover $M(\bar{e}')$ is constructed subject to the constraint that it *not* contain e'; $\bar{e}'$ is used to suggest that e' is *not* included in the solution.

Clearly the minimum for the original problem is either $M(e')$, or $M(\bar{e}')$ whichever has the lower cost.

This ends the informal description of the single-output extraction algorithm.

Example. Let us continue with the example of Figure 1.4 through 1.8. The first-order extremal set consists of

$$E(1) = a,d,q,t;$$

Also,

$$M(1)=E(1);$$

Next, we use the LT operation. It is easy to see that

$$e<i;\ h<l;\ m<i;\ p<l;$$

and, using lexicographical order,

$$c<b;\ s<r;$$

Now $Z(1)$ consists of all prime cubes, a through t.   Then $P(2)=Z(1)\text{-}E(1)$ and, deleting the cubes less than others,

$$Z(2)=b,f,g,i,j,k,l,n,o,r;$$

Figure 1.5 shows the complex from which first-order extremals are removed and Figure 1.6 shows it after LT is performed. The second-order extremals then consist of

$$E(2) = b,i,l,r;$$

as depicted in Figure 1.6. Then $M(2)=M(1) \cup E(2)$;

Fig. 1.4 A cubical complex
$Z(1)$

Fig. 1.5 $Z(1)$ with first-order
extremals removed

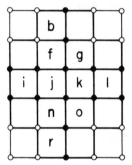

Fig. 1.6 $Z(2)$ with $<$-cubes
removed

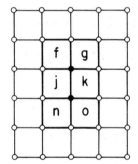

Fig. 1.7 $Z(2)$ with second-order
extremals removed

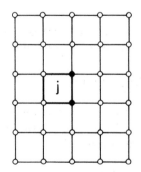

Fig. 1.8 Third-order extremal

Then LT is performed (see Figure 1.7). By lexicographical order or otherwise, all other cubes are less than j so that $Z(3)$ consists of j alone, (i.e., $Z3=j$) as shown in Figure 1.8. Thus j is the only third-order extremal, $E(3)=j$; Finally, the third cover,

$$M(3)=M(2) \cup E(3),$$

constitutes a final cover for the original problem.

We now give an example to exhibit the branching part of the extraction algorithm.

Example. The cubical complex is illustrated in Figure 1.9.

In this example, the prime cubes $Z(1)$ consist of cubes a,b,c,d,e,f, none of which are extremals. Thus

$$E(1)=\phi.$$

In this event we are forced to perform the branching operation. Branching is (arbitrarily) chosen to take place on cube a.

In the first solution a is treated as if it were an extremal, so that $M(1)=a$, leaving the complex shown in Figure 1.10 consisting of b,c,d,e,f. (Closed dots indicate vertices to be covered.) The LT operation shows $f<e$ and $b<c$. This leaves c,d,e, as shown in Figure 1.11. Here c and e are second-order extremals, yielding the first solution a,c,e. For simplicity assume this has a cost of 3.

To obtain the second constrained solution, the same cube a is treated as if it were less than some other prime cube and deleted from $Z(1)$. Then as depicted in Figure 1.12, b and f become extremals,

$$M(1)=b,f;$$

$$P(2)=c,d,e;$$

Here

$$c<d, e<d;$$

leaving

$$Z(2)=d;$$

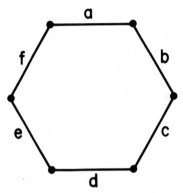

Fig. 1.9 The prime cubes $Z(1)$
(no extremals)

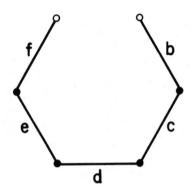

Fig. 1.10 Complex $Z(2)$
(a treated as extremal)

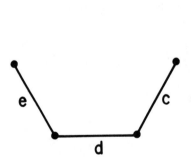

Fig. 1.11 Complex with
LT-cubes removed

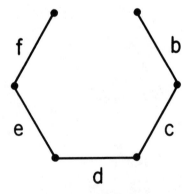

Fig. 1.12 Complex from which a
has been removed

thus d becomes a second-order extremal, yielding the second constrained solution

$$M(2)=b,d,f;$$

we thus have two constrained solutions, either of which may be an absolute minimum, whichever has lower cost. For this problem both solutions have the same cost, so that either is a minimum.

Exercise. Consider the following complex (devised by Ann Hardy) consisting of 12 prime cubes in a 9-dimensional space, as depicted in Figure 1.13.

0x010101x	(1)
0x0101x11	(2)
000x0101x	(3)
000x01x11	(4)
00000x01x	(5)
00000xx11	(6)
0000000xx	(7)
000000xx1	(8)
0000xx111	(9)
00x01x111	(10)
0000x01x1	(11)
00x0101x1	(12)

Compute the extremals and find a minimum cover.

This completes the description of the single-output extraction algorithm. We now briefly describe the generalization to the multiple-output case.

1.4. Extraction Algorithm, Multiple-output Case. Cubes have previously been defined for the multiple-output case. For clarity the extraction algorithm will be described in an algorithmic notation.

Again let $C(1)$ denote the ON-CARE conditions, $C(1)=CON$. Let $M(1)$ denote the initial partial solution.

Again the first step is to form the "space" $Z(1)$ of prime cubes. The multiple-output universal cube Q has all xs for its input part and all 1s for its output part. If # denotes the #-algorithm, Q the universal

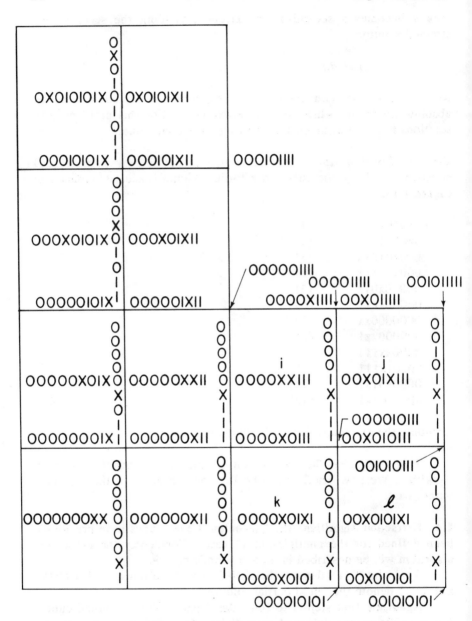

Fig 1.13 Complex in a 9-dimensional cube

cube and $DOFF$, a cover of the pure OFF-conditions with output zeros changed to ones, then the first step would be written

1) $Z(1)= (Q\#DOFF)$;

Another method of formation of $Z(1)$ is to perform the #-algorithm for each output individually and then to compose the single-output prime cubes into the multiple output prime cubes $Z(1)$. This method is applicable to large problems and is generally superior there. The #-algorithm is far more efficient than the *-algorithm for the same purpose (1958 Roth, 1967 Perlman, 1971 Beister).

The next step is to compute the space $E(1)$ of first-order extremals. If $C(1)$ denotes the cover of the ON-CARE conditions, and XT denotes the extraction procedure, then the extremal process is denoted

2) $E(1)=XT(Z(1),C(1))$;

the result is a function of $Z(1)$ and $C(1)$.

The extremals in the multiple-output case must be treated differently from those in the single-output case. Again an extremal is a prime cube which covers a vertex not covered by any other prime cube. If e is a multiple-output extremal, it can only be guaranteed that the output cofaces containing distinguished vertices - the vertices covered only by extremals e of the prime cubes - must belong, or one of its faces, must belong to every minimum cover. A precise statement is as follows:

Proposition. Let e be an extremal. Then a cover of the portion of e covered only by e of the prime cubes is $(e\#(Z-e))$ I $C(1)$. Let this be $a1 \mid b1,...,an \mid bn$. Let $e=e1 \mid e2$. Then a minimum cover of $C(1)$ may contain the face $f=e1 \mid (b1$ $I...I$ $bn)$.

Proof. First of all we claim that every minimum cover must contain every extremal e or one of its output faces. For by definition an extremal covers a CARE vertex that no other prime cube covers. Thus, if a minimum cover does not contain $e=e1 \mid e$ then it must contain a face $f1 \mid f2$ of e. But face $e1 \mid f2$ contains $f1 \mid f2$ and costs no more. Thus $e1 \mid f2$ can belong to a minimum cover. Q.E.D.

Now consider the cover $a1 \mid b1,...,an \mid bn$ of the distinguished vertices of e. By the above we know that every minimum cover must contain an output face of e (or e itself). But

$$e1 \mid (b1 \; I \; b2 \; I \; ... \; I \; bn)$$

is clearly the cheapest possible face of e. Q.E.D.

Thus for the multiple-output case only the portion f of the extremal is added to the developing solution. Let $F(1)$ denote the set of "critical" faces of each extremal that by the above proposition may be included in a minimum cover. Then the second partial solution

$$M(2) = M(1) \; \cup \; F(1)$$

and the new CARE conditions $C(2)$ remaining to be covered are

$$C(2) = C(1) \# F(1).$$

Let us denote this function as DEL (for DELete), so that we may write

$$F = DEL(CON,Z).$$

Let e be an extremal. Let f be its critical portion. Let g denote the cover of $e\#f$, the noncritical portions of e, a cover of the nondistinguished vertices of e. Finally let G denote the union of all such covers for every extremal e in $E(1)$. Then G is the portion of E which is not a direct part of the distinguished portion of E. As such it must be added to the prime cubes in the newly defined problem:

$$P(2) \; = \; (Z(1) \; \cup \; G)\text{-}E(1).$$

LESS-THAN operation. Next we perform the LESS-THAN operation LT. The definitions are the same as for the single-output case except that $P(2)$ for the multiple-output contains G, the noncritical portions of the extremals E. Again we say, for v and w elements of $P(2)$, $v<w$, if 1) the dimension of v is less than or equal to the dimension of w and 2) $v \; I \; C(2)$ is contained in w. In that case a minimum, as shown above, may be obtained without use of v: v may be deleted from the prime cubes $P(2)$. Let $Z(2)$ denote $P(2)$ from which have been delet-

ed all cubes v for which $v<w$ for some w in $P(2)$. If $v<w$ and $w<v$ let lexicographical order choose one for deletion.

Second Stage. The second stage of the multiple-output extraction algorithm, under the assumption that $E(1)\neq\phi$, is a recursion on the extraction procedure

$$E(2)=XT(Z(2),C(2));$$

$$M(3)=M(2) \cup F(2);$$

where $F(2)$ is the collection of critical faces of extremals of $E(2)$;

$$C(3)=C(2)\#F(2);$$

$$G(2)=E(2)\#F(2);$$

letting $G(2)$ denote the portion of each extremal, for all extremals, that is not a part of their distinguished portion, we have

$$P(3) = (Z(2) \cup G(2))\text{-}E(2);$$

and so on until a solution is obtained: $CON\#M(i)=\phi$; unless, at some stage before this end, no new extremals are uncovered, $E(i)=\phi$, in which case the branching mode is invoked.

In the multiple output case of branching one must select, in addition to a prime cube, one of its critical output faces. Let SEL denote the process of selection for the cube $a \mid b$, and g its output face selected to be distinguished

$$(a \mid b,g)=SEL(Z).$$

In order to clarify the multiple-output extraction algorithm, we shall describe it in algorithmic form, in the so-called regular notation, which will be summarized in the next section.

1.5   Regular Algorithmic Notation, R-notation. The R-notation developed as a generalization of the cubical notation. An *executional statement* is of the form

$$(c1,...,cs) = F(a1,...,ar);$$

where the ai are the domain or input variables, F is the function symbol and ci are the range or output symbols. A *conditional statement* has the form

$$(u=a)\Rightarrow((d1,...,dt) = H(e1,...,eu));$$

this has the interpretation that if $u=a$ (the condition) then $(d1,..,dt) = H(e1,...,eu)$ holds. A statement whether executional or conditional, is referred to as an *R-statement*. We substitute the symbol $\Rightarrow$ for | for cubes, in interest of clarity.

An *R-formula* is a string of R-statements written in the following format: First comes the left angular bracket $<$, then the *name* of the R-formula, consisting of the names of the output variables, $(j1,...,ju)$ enclosed in parentheses followed by the equality sign, the formula name, the formula input variables enclosed in parentheses $(k1,...,kt)$, followed by the equality sign plus a colon =: followed by the string of R-statements, each enclosed in round brackets, all terminated by a right angular bracket $>$.

$$<(j1,...,ju)=J(k1,...,kt)=: (R1)(R2)...(Rm)>$$

An *R-algorithm* is a string of R-formulas. The *name* of the R-algorithm E is written before the R-string in the form $(e1,...,es)=E(g1,...,gr)$ where the gi are primitive arguments of the R-statements and R-formulas, i.e. arguments which are not themselves the values of R-formulas or R-statements, and the es are the values of the algorithm.

Then the multiple-output extraction algorithm assumes the following form in R-notation.

$$<(M,Z)=XT(CON,DOFF,S)=:(CON\#S=0\Rightarrow S)(Z=\#(Q,DOFF)$$
$$(M,Z',E)=E(CON,S,Z')>$$

$$<(M,Z',E)=E(CON,S,Z'))=: CON\#S=\phi\Rightarrow M=S)$$

$$(Z'=LT(Z,CON)(E=XT(Z',CON))$$

$$(E=\phi\Rightarrow B(Z',CON)(F=DEL(Z',CON))(G=E\#F)$$

$$E(CON\#F,S \cup F,Z'\text{-}E \cup G)>$$

$$<B(CON,S,Z')=:((a\mid b),g)=SEL(Z))(h=(a\mid b)\#g)$$

$$(M(g)=E(CON\#g,M \cup g,Z-((a\mid b) \cup h)))$$

$$(M(\overline{g})=E(CON,M,Z\text{-}a\mid b \cup h))$$

$$(c(M(g))<c(M(\overline{g})\Rightarrow M=M(g))$$

$$(c(M(g)>c(M(\overline{g})\Rightarrow M=M(\overline{g})))>$$

1.6   Program Runs.   MIN370 is a PL/I program using the above R-algorithmic description (written by Leroy Junker of the IBM T. J. Watson Research Center) of the multiple-output extraction algorithm whose option is termed EXACT.   Other options are provided. SHRINK, under the name COFACE, may be run as an option.

There is a variation of the extraction algorithm called PSEUDO in which each extremal is thrown into the developing solution *in toto*.   In general it does not obtain a minimum but comes close, at a fraction of the computing cost.

The option TRUNC=i under options EXACT or PSEUDO causes the computation to terminate after the ith solution has been formed. The cost function COSTFN could be: UNITCOST, a cost of one for each cube; or STANDARD, one for each input and output (not x) for each cube.   The option CSTMIN=c will drop any developing solution if its cost exceeds c.

A problem having an ON-array of 15 multiple-output cubes of cost 82, of a binary adder was run under the EXACT mode of MIN370, with standard cost function.   The computed minimum cover cost was 43.   Its listing is shown as Figure 1.14.   Compute time on the IBM System 360 Model 91 was 0.2 seconds.

A larger problem was run for California Institute of Technology's NASA Jet Propulsion Laboratory.   This had 8 inputs and 8 outputs, with 192 cubes in the initial cover, with cost 2560.   The final solution obtained under SHRINK contained 66 cubes, cost 637, with running time (S/360 M/91) of 27 seconds.

In a larger problem, the "Tape Code Translator" with 16 inputs and 6 outputs, from an initial cover of 150 cubes with no DON'T-CARE conditions, MIN370 computed the 72 prime cubes in 86.5 seconds, and went on to get an exact minimum in 198 seconds on the IBM/360 model 91.   Cost at one per cube was reduced from 150 to 50.

CIRCUIT MINIMIZATION:

BINARY ADDER (ON ARRAY) 9-1

TITLE='NO__TITLE';
OPTION='EXACT'

COSTFN='STANDARD'

TRUNC=   0;
    COST OF EACH 0-INPUT=   1.00
    COST OF EACH 1-INPUT=   1.00
    COST OF EACH 1-OUTPUT=   1.00
        ALLOCATING   1000 CUBES FOR Z, 1000 CUB
            1000 CUBES FOR CSS

    15 CARE-CUBES:
            0001 | XX1
            0010 | X1X
            0011 | X11
            0100 | XX1
            0101 | X1X
            0110 | X11
            0111 | 1XX
            1000 | X1X
            1001 | X11
            1010 | 1XX
            1011 | 1X1
            1100 | X11
            1101 | 1XX
            1110 | 1X1
            1111 | 11X
                    COST OF C=   82.00

    0 DON'T-CARE CUBES:

    THERE ARE   17 PRIME CUBES.
                    COST OF PRIME CUBES=
        TIME TAKE TO COMPUTE PRIME CUBES=

    MINIMUM COVER: 11 CUBES.
                X0X1 | XX1
                001X | X1X
                0X10 | X1X
                X1X0 | XX1
                0101 | X1X
                X111 | 1XX
                100X | X1X
                1X00 | X1X
                1X1X | 1XX
                11X1 | 1XX
                1111 | X1X
                        COST=   43.00
                        NUMBER OF BR

                        MAXIMUM DEPTH

                        EXTRACTION TIME=   0.
        TOTAL TIME (INCLUDING PRIME-CUBE CALC.)= 0.14

        Fig. 1.14. MIN370 Output for a Binary Adder

1.7. Decreasing the Size of Associative Logic Arrays. In associative logic arrays, or in a programmed logic array, logic is sometimes represented in three levels as well as two.   Obtaining a three-level solution is viewed in terms of factoring a two-level cover into three.   By use of the technique to be described, the cost of a two-level cover of a four-bit byte arithmetic and logic unit ALU was cut in half, no absolute three-level minimum guaranteed.

The technique is essentially constituted of two portions.   One of these portions involves a product suitably termed the *combo product* of two cubes.   It seeks pairs of cubes which have the property that they differ in precisely two coordinates.   The combo product is defined such that each of the possible differences, in the two coordinates in which they differ, can be identified.   For example, 1x would be A; x1, B; 01, C; 10, D; 0x, E; and x0, F.

The combo product of two or more cubes (there could be three which would so combine) contains all of the information contained in the original cubes so combined.   Consequently, they may be eliminated from subsequent combinations, except for the fact that one particular cube is combined and "combo producted" with one or two other cubes and, therefore, the question would be which of the various combo products to use to cover the original cube.

Such formulation amounts to a covering problem in the classical sense, as discussed above.   In this formulation, the cubes themselves may be thought of as vertices and the combo products as 1-cubes having the appropriate subcubes as vertices.

In carrying out this technique, the combo product of each pair of cubes is taken to which there is then added any stage at which a new combo product has been made.   The two original cubes constituting the original combo product are deleted and the new combo product inserted in their place.   Such new combo products can then be combo producted with other cubes.   There results thereby an assemblage of cubes, i.e., the associative logic array which defines some function, i.e., some realization of a function.

Each cube in this array can be considered a vertex of a graph. Thus, if two such cubes have a combo product P, then these are considered to be vertices of the 1-cube consisting of the product P.   There is thereby provided a graph and the problem which is presented is the obtaining of a "cover" of the vertices by the cells, which are the edges of the graph in such manner that a minimum number of these occur. The "covering problem" can be solved in the manner of the extraction algorithm as described above.   However, for the purposes of expediency and efficiency, the extraction algorithm is truncated to obtain a nonredundant cover. Such truncation is accomplished as follows.

Let it be assumed in a first instance that all combo products are formed. Those cubes which are covered by exactly one combo product are then found. The latter combo products are extremals in the sense of the extraction algorithm and have to be included in every minimum cover.

A "less than" operation is then performed. In this operation, combo product A is less than combo product B if all of the vertices of combo product A which are not covered by the extrema so far calculated are covered by those of combo product B. Thus, this step uncovers a "second order" of extrema, which have the property that they cover vertices not covered by any of those remaining, etc. This step continues until a solution has been obtained or else no new extrema occur in going through the less-than operation. Since, in this situation, branching has to take place, any expedient algorithm for selecting a pseudo-extremum to continue to the end of the operation is employed. If an exact solution is desired, then recursion is performed as in the extraction algorithm to find an exact minimum.

In a second situation, a nonredundant cover is obtained. To this end, the extrema are computed and then, from these computed extrema, decisions are made as to which are to be obtained. (Cf. 1974 Roth).

For example in the 6-variable cover shown below, only three combo products are nontrivial, as shown below the horizontal dividing line; each are extremals and together they cover the original cubes.

```
    1100xx
    1111xx
    00011x
    0001x1
    101011
    011011
    ‾‾‾‾‾‾
    11CCxx
    0001AB
    DC1011
```

1.8. Other Work. One of the first works in the field of two-level single-output minimization was that of Quine (1955), who developed a logical interpretation of the problem. The algorithms presented were considered, however, to be inefficient (Nelson (1953)). McCluskey (1956) developed an arithmetization and improvement of Quine's method, which was extended by McCluskey and Schorr (1962) to the multiple-output case. See also the work of Bartee (1961). Comparisons at the Jet Propulsion Laboratory indicated that Bartee's technique was not as efficient as the extraction algorithm (1967).

The above R-algorithmic description was used by Leon Levy (1974 Roth and Levy) to define an APL program realizing the algorithm. Leroy Junker (1978, Junker, Roth) wrote a PL/I program (MIN370 cf. below) on the same basis. In Chapter 4 a compiler for transforming an R-algorithm into logic is outlined. Halliwell defined a subset PL/R of PL/I realizing a subset of the R-notation restricted to bit strings and logical operations, together with a compiler RTRAN transforming PL/R and DO algorithms into R-designs. In chapter 9 is described means to transform R-algorithms into an iterative logic structure.

An interesting rendition of the 5-*cube* was given by Frisiani (1965), Fig. 1.15.

Problems

1.1. Find the interface of x1x0 | 1x1 and 1xx0 | x11.

1.2. Let 001x, x1x1, 01x1, 0000, xx00 be a cover C. Find the cofaces of 001x with respect to C. Repeat for 0000.

1.3. Find the prime cubes of C in Problem 1.2 using the double sharp method.

1.4. List all cubes of the complex defined by the cover 1xx1, 0x1x.

1.5. Perform the CONTAIN operation to remove cubes from the cover 1x1x | 1x, 1x1x | 11, 0x00 | 1x, 0000 | 11.

1.6. Form the #-products

$$(1xx1)\#x11x$$

$$0x1x\#1x11$$

$$01x1 \mid x1\#x1x1 \mid x11$$

$$xxxx\#1010$$

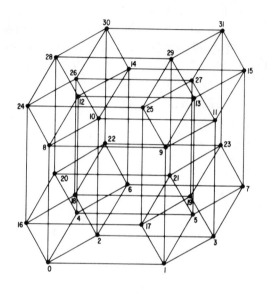

Fig. 1.15 Frisiani's rendition of *5-cube*

1.7. Let c=1x1x|1x1 and C=1010|111, 0xxx|111, 1x11|11x. Perform c#C.

1.8. Let C=000, 100, 110, 111, 011, 010 be a cover. Find an approximate cover using SHRINK.

1.9. Perform SHRINK on the following ON- and OFF-covers 1x10|1, 0000|1; x100|0.

1.10. Remove redundant cube(s) in the cover xx111 | 1x, x1x1x | 11, x01x1 | 1x, 0x111 | 1x.

1.11. Compute the prime cubes of the ON-complex plus the DON'T-CAREs by forming the #-product of Q with the modified OFF-cover $DOFF$ = 1010x | 11, 01x1x | 1x, 0000 | 11, x0x0x | x1.

1.12. Prove the first Proposition on page 16.

1.13. Prove the second Proposition on page 16.

1.14. Perform the LESS-THAN LT operation on the following cover

$$
\begin{array}{l}
101x1x \\
x01x1x \\
1xx1x0 \\
1xx11x \\
100xxx
\end{array}
$$

where the CARE conditions are

$$
\begin{array}{l}
1x1x1x \\
x0x0x0
\end{array}
$$

1.15. Form the crown of the following cubes

$$
\begin{array}{l}
101x10x0 \\
x11111x0 \\
0x101xx0 \\
011011x0
\end{array}
$$

1.16. Using the extraction algorithm find the multiple-output minimum of the following problem

$$
\begin{array}{l}
xx1x \mid 1x1 \\
x100 \mid x1x \\
x101 \mid x1x \\
x111 \mid x1x \\
x110 \mid x1x \\
0000 \mid 111
\end{array}
$$

with no DON'T-CARE conditions.

1.17. Find a 3-level reduction of the solution to Problem 1.16 using the method of Section 1.5.

Bibliography

1852. Boole, George, "An Investigation of the Laws of Thought", *The Open Court Publishing Company* (1916). Reprinted by *Dover Publications* 1951.

1938. Shannon, C. E., "A Symbolic Analysis of Relay and Switching Circuits", *Transactions, AIEE* vol. 57, pp. 713-723.

1952. Veitch, E. W., "A Chart Method for Simplifying Truth Functions", *Proc. Assoc. for Computing Machinery* (Richard Rimbach Associates, Pittsburgh), pp. 127-133.

1953. Karnaugh, M., "The Map Method for Synthesis of Combinational Logic Circuits", *Communications and Electronics* No. 9, pp. 593-599.

1953. Nelson, Raymond L., "Review of Quine's Paper", *Journal of Symbolic Logic*, vol. 18, pp. 280-283.

1955. Quine, W. V., "A Way to Simplify Truth Functions", *American Mathematical Monthly*, vol. 62, pp. 627-631.

1956. Roth, J. Paul, "Algebraic Topological Methods for the Synthesis of Switching Circuits in n Variables", The Institute for Advanced Study, Princeton, N. J. Electronic Computer Project, Technical Report, No. 56-02, April.

1956. McCluskey, E. J., "Minimization of Boolean Functions", *Bell Syst. Tech. J.*, vol. 35, pp. 1417-1444, June.

1957. Roth, J. Paul, "Two Logical Minimization Problems", *Proceedings of Summer Institute on Symbolic Logic, American Mathematical Society*. Reissued by Institute for Defense Analysis, Princeton, N. J, 1960, pp. 396-401. Cf. also IBM Research Report, RA-45, 1972.

1958. Roth, J. Paul, "Algebraic Topological Methods for the Synthesis of Switching Systems", *Transactions of American Mathematical Society*, vol. 88, pp. 301-326.

1958. Ritz, Robert, Personal communication.

1959. Roth, J. Paul, "Algebraic Topological Methods in Synthesis", *Annals of Computation Laboratory, Harvard University Press*, vol. 29, pp. 57-73.

1959. Roth, J. Paul, "Una Teoria per la progettazione dei Meccanismi Automatici," *Centro Internazionale Matematico Estivo*, Varenna, Italy, printed by the University of Rome.

1961. Bartee, T. C., "Computer Design of Multiple Output Logical Networks", *IRE Transactions on Electronic Computers*, vol. EC-10, pp. 21-30.

1961. Randlev, Ann C., E. G. Wagner, J. Paul Roth, "Algorithms for Logical Design", *AIEE Transactions on Communications and Electronics*, vol. 56, pp. 450-458.

1962. McCluskey, E. J. and H. Schorr, "Essential Multiple-Output Prime Implicants," Proceedings of Symposium on Mathematical Theory of Automata, *Polytechnic Press of the Polytechnic Institute of Brooklyn*, pp. 437-457.

1965. Frisiani, Arrigo L., "Fondamenti dei Procedimenti Topologici per la Semplificazione della Funzioni Booleane", *Atti dell Accademia Ligure di Scienze e Lettere*, Genova, Italy, Vol. 22, pp. 1-33.

1967. Perlman, M. Personal Communication.

1968. Roth, J. P., "A Calculus and an Algorithm for the Multiple-Output 2-level Minimization Problem", IBM Thomas J. Watson Research Center, Yorktown Heights, N.Y. 10598 RC 2007, 11 pp.

1968. Wagner, Eric G., "An Axiomatic Treatment of Roth's Extraction Algorithm", IBM Thomas J. Watson Research Center, Yorktown Heights, N.Y. 10598, RC 2205.

1968. Roth, J. Paul and E. G. Wagner, "A Calculus and an Algorithm for a Logic Minimization Problem together with an Algorithmic Notation", IBM Thomas J. Watson Research Center, Yorktown Heights, N.Y. 10598, RC 2280, 64 pp.

1968. Levy, Leon, "An APL Program for the Multiple-Output Two-level Minimization Problem", IBM Thomas J. Watson Research Center, Yorktown Heights, NY 10598, RC 2323.

1968. Wagner, Eric G., "An Axiomatic Treatment of Roth's Extraction Algorithm", IBM Thomas J. Watson Research Center, Yorktown Heights, NY 10598, RC 2205.

1969. Roth, J. P. and M. Perlman, "Space Applications of a Minimization Algorithm", *IEEE Transactions on Aerospace and Electronic Systems*, vol. AES 5, pp. 703-711.

1971. Beister, J., Karlsruhe University. Letter to M. Perlman.

1974. Ellozy, H. A., B. A. Lewis, and J. P. Roth, "Generation of Associative Logic Arrays", *IBM Technical Disclosure Bulletin*, vol. 17, pp. 1249-1253.

1974. Roth, J. P., "Decreasing the Size of Associative Logic Arrays", *IBM Technical Disclosure Bulletin*, vol. 17, pp. 1252-1253.

1975. Fleisher, H. and L. I. Maissel, "An Introduction to Array Logic", *IBM Journal of Research and Development*, vol. 19, pp. 98-109.

1976. Holtzman, Ernest, GE R&D Center, Schenectady, N.Y. Personal communication.

1978. Roth, J. P., "Programmed Logic Array Optimization", *IEEE Transactions on Computers*, vol. C-27, pp. 174-176.

1978. Junker, Leroy and J. Paul Roth, "User's Guide to a Program for Multiple-Output Array-Logic Minimization", IBM Thomas J. Watson Research Center, Yorktown Heights, NY 10598, RC 6894.

1978. Junker, L. V. and J. P. Roth, "A New Differencing Operation for Multiple Output Functions", *IBM Technical Disclosure Bulletin*, vol. 21, pp. 1307-1309.

Chapter 2

ACYCLIC LOGIC

Introduction. Computer hardware in its functional aspects is represented by logic, in the form of a design. A logic design is constructed from primitive logic functions, *devices,* through their interconnection. First we discuss primitives.

2.1.   Logic Primitives. Each technology has devices effecting certain transformations between various physical quantities, which are expressible as binary variables; the relation then becomes a logical function. Usually this function has a few input variables and one output variable.

   A 2-input And-Invert AI is a typical example. In general the function defined by a primitive logic block will be expressed as a (2-level) cover, as described in Chapter 1. For this AI we have, naming the input variables a and b and the output, c,

$$
\begin{array}{cc|c}
a & b & c \\
1 & 1 & 0 \\
0 & x & 1 \\
x & 0 & 1 \\
\end{array}
$$

Here the first row of the cover $11 \mid 0$ denotes that when both a and b are 1 the output c is 0. The second cube indicates that if a is 0 then, regardless of the value of b, c will be 1. Similarly the third cube in the cover denotes that if $b=0$ then, independently of the value of a, c is 1. A logic function or block such as the 2-input AI just described is represented, as shown in Fig. 2.1, by a box with line segments directed toward the box to denote inputs, and a line segment directed away from the box, to denote its output. The direction of flow convention in this text will be from left to right unless otherwise specified by arrows. Similarly top-down direction is assumed unless otherwise specified.

A 4-input AI would be defined by the cover 1111 | 0, 0xxx | 1, x0xx | 1, xx0x | 1, xxx0 | 1; where variable names are understood. This would similarly be represented by an AI box, with four input lines and one output line. An And block A, of two inputs, would be given as 11 | 1; 0x | 0; x0 | 0, with variables a,b,c understood. An Exclusive-Or Xor is given as 10 | 1, 01 | 1, 00 | 0, 11 | 0. The function Or is given as 00 | 0, 1x | 1, x1 | 1. A simplest function is the *Invert*, denoted I or N (for Negate); in this discussion N will be used. This has the truth table, cover, of 1 | 0, 0 | 1 depicted in Fig. 2.2; here and elsewhere the bar over the variable indicates negation.

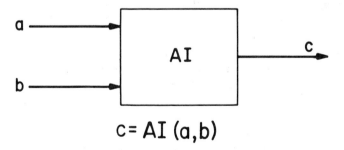

$$c = AI\ (a,b)$$

Fig. 2.1. A logic block AI

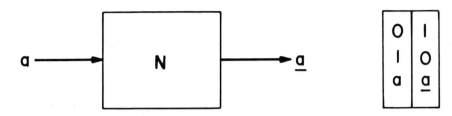

Fig. 2.2 Negate function N

2.2. Logic Composition. A logic design is formed by the interconnection of logic blocks, that is, by the identification of certain inputs of one block with outputs of others. For example, Fig. 2.3 shows the interconnection of two Ands A with an *Or* Or. Here the inputs *a, b, c, d* of the And circuits are called *primary inputs* PIs - they are not fed by any other blocks - and *g* is termed a *primary output* PO - it is arbitrarily so designated.

We represent a logic design by an individual local cover, one for each primitive, as in Chapter 1. A name is attached to each primitive, each block, used. This name is also given to the line emanating from the block. In general the output line will be connected to, i.e. will "drive", more than one other block. We assume here that each primitive, block, has exactly one output variable. We allow for *fan-out*, i.e. copies of the same output. This induces an assignment of a name to each variable of each cover. See the local cover, one for each line, of Fig. 2.3. These local covers *define* the overall function of the logic design; see Section 2.7 for description of an algorithm, *P** (pronounced PISTAR), to go from local covers to a single cover expressed solely in terms of PI and PO variables.

The majority function MAJ is a function of three binary variables; if at least two inputs are 1 it has the value 1; otherwise, 0. This is realized in Fig 2.4, with three 2-input Ands having cover 11 | 1; 0x | 0; x0 | 0 and with a 3-input Or, defined by the cover 000 | 0, 1xx | 1, x1x | 1, xx1 | 1;

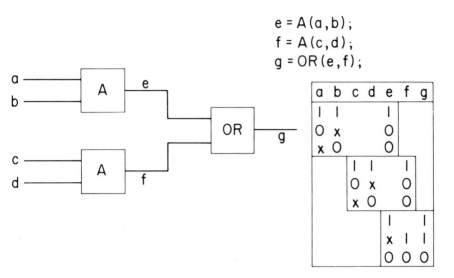

$$e = A(a,b);$$
$$f = A(c,d);$$
$$g = OR(e,f);$$

Fig. 2.3 And/Or circuit, functional expression and local cover

More complicated is the PARITY function of four input variables; it determines whether there is an odd or even number of positive
input signals (Fig. 2.5).   That two lines intersect will be indicated
throughout by a large dot at their intersection; two lines touching
without the dot are understood not to intersect.

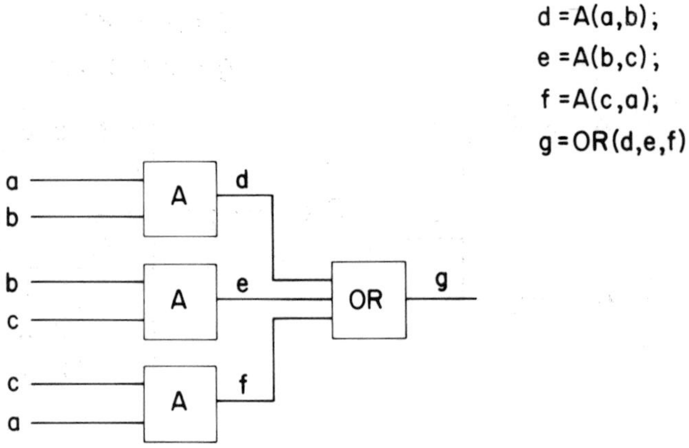
d =A(a,b);
e =A(b,c);
f =A(c,a);
g=OR(d,e,f)
a
b
A
d
b
c
A
e
OR
g
c
a
A
f

Fig. 2.4. Majority function

We allow arbitrary interconnections in forming logic designs except that in Chapters 2 and 3 we do not allow cycles, i.e. no feedback.

2.3. Function of Acyclic Logic Design. As stated above, a *primary input* PI is a variable which is not, in the logic given, a function of any other variable in the design. *Primary outputs POs* can be any variables so designated. In general a logic design may have several POs. Variables or lines which are neither PIs nor POs are called *internal variables.*

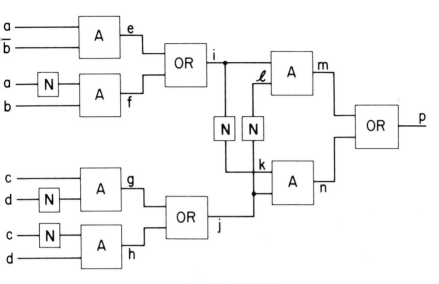

Fig. 2.5. 4-bit PARITY

An acyclic logic design with p primary inputs and q primary outputs defines a function mapping "words" of p bits into words of q bits. To define its behavior, it is necessary only to examine sequences of inputs, words, of length one, for it has no memory.

2.4.   Fan-in and Fan-out. In general it is possible for a given variable, line, to *feed* or to be an argument of several primitive functions or variables, which may be internal or primary-output variables.   The number of primitives a given variable feeds in a design is termed its *fan-out*. The number of variables feeding a primitive is termed its *fan-in*. The maximum fan-in and fan-out are determined by the technology; typically these numbers might be 4 and 10 respectively. The fan-out, for instance, of the variable a in Fig. 2.5 is 2. The fan-in of each block, except for the Inverts, is 2.

2.5.   Level. Along any path from a PI to a PO the number of blocks traversed is its *level* number. The maximum over all such paths is the *level number* of the logic. Speed of operation depends upon this number: the fewer the faster.

2.6.   Segmentation. A simple procedure which substantially reduces computations of several design algorithms is called *segmentation*. In this process we select subdesigns, one for each PO, consisting of all primitives that feed a given PO, directly or indirectly, and *only* such logic: this is called a *segment*. This simple transformation has a substantial effect on computation time for many algorithms.

2.7.   *P*:* Many Levels to Two Levels. In Chapter 1 we dealt with a method of expression of functions which could be thought of as two levels of logic: each cube representing an acyclic gate of its bound inputs and cubes with a common output ORed together. (There are other ways of representing the function in two levels, e.g. AIs followed by AIs.) In this chapter we treat functional compositions having in general many levels of logic - as yet *sans* feedback. How can the two representations, 2-level and multi-level, be reconciled?   Here we give means, the *P**-algorithm (pronounced PISTAR), for going from a multiple-level design to an equivalent design having just two levels (1960).   They are equivalent in the sense that they define the same function.   (Equivalence of covers may be decided by use of the #-operation, c.f. Chapter 1, or verification procedures, Chapter 6). Before proceeding to a formal description of *P**, we shall use it in some examples.

Our first example of *P** is the Exclusive-Or with implementation depicted in Fig. 2.6. (It is a part of the 4-bit parity of Fig. 2.5 and is itself a 2-bit parity.) This design has three levels of logic; a and b are its Primary Inputs PIs, and g is its single primary output PO.   For single output functions, it is not uncommon to designate the cubes of the cover all having (output) value 1, as the ON-cover. Similarly the cubes having value 0 define the OFF-cover. The *P**-algorithm develops its ON-cover and OFF-cover concurrently but, for simplicity, we shall develop only the ON-cover.

We start with the PO g and write covering conditions for which its output has the value 1, namely $g=1$. Then as shown in the table of Fig. 2.6, we make the substitution $P^*{:}g=\text{Or}(e,f)$, in terms of its ON-cover.

First, however, imagine that we are in the space of variables a,b,c,d,e,f,g and that our transformations take place within this space. The first "injection" operator exchanges a cover expressed in terms of g alone into one in terms of e and f.

This is effected by substituting, for the cube $\overset{g}{1}$, the cubes

$$
\begin{array}{c}
ef \\
1x \\
x1
\end{array}
$$

to which $\overset{g}{1}$ is equivalent by the definition of the circuit. This substitution is expressed symbolically by the operator $P^*{:}g=\mathrm{Or}(e,f)$. In similar fashion (cf. Fig. 2.6) the operator $P^*{:}\ f=A(b,d)$ expresses the substitu-

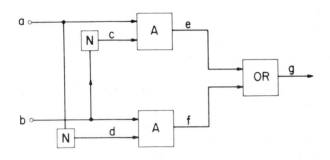

Fig. 2.6. *P*-operation going from design in 3 levels to 2*

tion for variable f the And of b and d. This is performed on each cube of the above array, (by substituting: the ON-array for f in each cube where f has value 1; the OFF-array, for value 0 and xs otherwise, subject to interface with the remaining component of the cube). Here we obtain

> bde
> xx1
> 11x

Similarly the successive substitutions $P^*{:}d=\mathrm{N}(a)$, $P^*{:}c=\mathrm{N}(b)$ express the substitution of variables a and b (the primary input variables) for d and c respectively.

Exercise: Perform the P^*-operation for the circuit in Fig. 2.6. Devise rules for the case in which the variables from previous stages intersect with the newly introduced variables.

The result gives a cover of the PO in terms of the PIs alone as shown in Fig. 2.6.

Let us consider another example, Fig. 2.7. This figure shows a 3-level logic circuit constructed essentially by Peter R. Schneider as a counterexample to a conjecture in test generation; cf. Chapter 3. Each block, or logic cell, is an AI with fan-in of 2 except for block 12, having fan-in 4. Fan-out is either 1 or 2. Observe that with respect to PO 12, segmentation effects no reduction, atypically, in the size of the logic. Segmentation does effect a reduction for circuits 8 and 11. We perform P^* for output 12.

The first transformation to be performed is P^* on the block $12=\mathrm{AI}(8,9,10,11)$. This means substituting for the 1 in column 12 the ON-cover 0xxx, x0xx, xx0x, xxx0, in coordinates 8,9,10,11 respectively. The second transformation, a product of four elementary transformations, consists in substituting new variables for 8,9,10,11: this is denoted

$P^*{:}[11=\mathrm{AI}(3,7);\ 10=\mathrm{AI}(4,6);\ 9=\mathrm{AI}(1,6);\ 8=\mathrm{AI}(2,5)].$

This yields the four cubes immediately following in the figure, starting with the cube having 1s in coordinates 3 and 7, blanks elsewhere.

The next transformation, actually a product of three elementary transformations, is

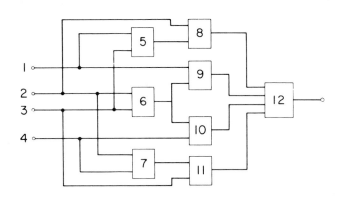

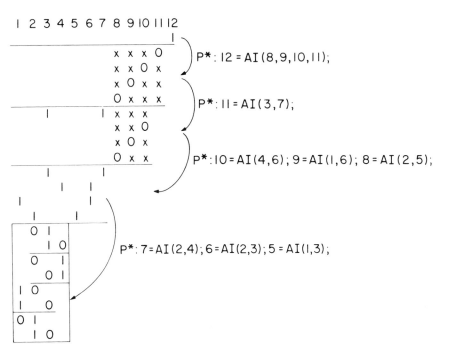

Fig. 2.7. Schneider's example - all blocks AIs

P^*: $[7=AI(2,4); \ 6=AI(2,3); \ 5=AI(1,3)]$.

This yields the final array of eight cubes expressed in terms of primary-input variables 1,2,3,4 alone.

Formal description of P^*. In this chapter we assume that a logic design has no feedback, hence has no sequential operation. The algorithm P^* accepts a multiple-level acyclic logic design and transforms it into a cover, equivalently, a 2-level realization in And-Or (or AI-AI, etc.) form. The algorithm may operate in the multiple-output mode or it may operate independently on the segment defined by each output variable. In the latter form, considerably less computer time and storage are required. We therefore use this mode.

Assume then with no loss of generality that a logic design has exactly one output and that every logic block feeds, directly or indirectly, the primary output PO.

The P^*-algorithm will be described recursively. Assume that for each block an ON- and an OFF-cover are given and assume that the blocks, lines, variables are labelled successively from the output with integers, the PO having the label 2 and all of the blocks feeding it having labels 3 through k where k-2 is the fan-in of the PO. All blocks are labelled successively in such manner that the label of each block exceeds that of its successor.

Starting with the first input to the PO we look at each cube u in the ON- and OFF-covers of the PO. If input 3 of this cube is a 1, cube u is replaced by r cubes, one for each cube of the ON-cover of 3 - where all coordinates of these cubes agree with those of u except for the input coordinates of block 3, which take on the values of its on-cover.

If input 3 contains a 0, then the above process is similarly performed for the OFF-cover of block 3.

If input 3 in the first cube of the ON-cover for the PO is an x, then this x is merely deleted. Optionally an x may be assigned to each coordinate input of 3 or they may be left blank.

Assume we have performed the P^*-algorithm for v-1 variables of the design - each variable has by construction a serial integer attached - ON-OFF-covers having been generated in terms of internal variables and possibly PIs. Then the above described process is performed on variable v. Assume further (induction hypothesis) that the cover (both

ON- and OFF-) is equivalent to the original cover for the construction for variable v-1.

There is, however, a complication that ensues. It might be that some input variable, say w, of v has, by previous operations, already been specified to be a 0 or 1. In a given cube if the w-input value of v coincides with that value, then no conflict exists and the value remains for a particular substitution of the ON- and OFF-covers. On the other hand, if there is a conflict between the values assigned by previous operations and that of variable v, then this cube must be dropped from the newly generated cover - it represents an inconsistency in the cover, the same variable repeated with inconsistent values.

The initial ON- OFF-covers for the PO, in terms of itself, are obviously valid. Assume by induction hypothesis that the P^*-operation up to stage v-1 is a valid representation of the function defined by the PO and its network. Now P^* at the vth stage is merely a valid substitution of input-variable, (2-level) representation for variable v. Thus P^* at the vth stage yields a valid representation. Therefore, by induction, the final expression yielded by P^* in terms of the PIs is valid. Q.E.D.

If one considers the space of all variables of a design, (input, output and internal variables), then the P^*-algorithm is seen as nothing more than successive applications of the interface operator of Chapter 1.

2.8.   Factorization. In the last section we showed how to transform from logic in several levels to two. Here we exhibit a method to go in the opposite direction, in part at least. The algorithm called COM-POSE operates on a 2-level cover and, searching recursively for commonality, produces an And/Or design not exceeding in levels the number prescribed by the user. It treats the multiple-output case. COMPOSE is used in conjunction with other algorithms to transform acyclic logic designs into high-level definitions thereof, in particular for R^* of Chapter 4. Logic can ordinarily be realized more economically in more than two levels. Furthermore the primitives of a technology invariably have limited fan-in - say four - necessitating in general multiple levels of logic.

The Method. Assume initially that the design to be factored is in the form of a 2-level multiple-output cover. A cube, a member of the cover, consists of an *input part,* consisting of 0s, 1s and xs, one such value for each input coordinate and an *output part,* consisting of a 1 or x for each output coordinate (part of the ON-array). The input part represents an And (conjunction) of each input variable whose coordinate is a 1 and its negation for each variable whose coordinate is a 0. A 1 in the output part indicates that the And block corresponding to the input part *drives* this particular output. An x in the output part indicates that this cube is not committed to the particular output.

The Mask Product. We wish to ascertain those input coordinates which the cubes of the cover have in common. For this purpose we define the *mask product* of two cubes. Consider cubes $c = c(1),...,c(r) | d(1),...,d(t)$ and $e = e(1),...,e(r) | f(1),...,f(t)$, where the $c(i)$ and $e(i)$ are the input parts of cubes c and e respectively and $d(j)$ and $f(j)$ are their respective output parts. The *coordinate input mask product m* is given first.

$$c(i) \ m \ e(i) \ = \ c(i) \ \text{if} \ c(i) \ = \ e(i)$$

$$= \ \text{x otherwise}$$

For the *coordinate output mask* product,

$$d(j) \ m \ f(j) \ = \ d(j) \ \text{if} \ d(j) \ = \ f(j) \ = \ 1$$

$$= \ \text{x otherwise.}$$

We now exhibit examples

$$(10x11 \,|\, 1x1x)m(101x0 \,|\, 111x) \ = \ (10xxx \,|\, 1x1x)$$

$$(11011xx \,|\, 1)m(1111000 \,|\, 1) \ = \ (11x1xxx \,|\, 1)$$

The Algorithm. The intent of the algorithm is to make nearly optimal selections of factorizations by use of the mask product. The algorithm will be described.

1.   The first step is to order the cubes of the cover according to the number of input coordinates with values 0 or 1.
2.   The mask product, *m-product*, of the first cube in this ordering is formed with each other cube in the cover.

Define the *goodness* of such a product to be the number of 1s and 0s it has in its input part.

3. Select a product whose goodness is a maximum.
4. Remove each cube forming this product and add this *m*-product to the cover.
5. If the cover is reduced to one element the algorithm ceases. Otherwise return to step 1 and order the cover, etc., or until a prescribed number of levels is reached.
6. After the initial factorization write down the factors used to construct the function and ascertain whether or not these factors have common factors, by formation of the mask-products as above.

Consider the following example consisting of eight cubes with input variables *a,b,c,d,e,f,g,h* and a single output (multiple outputs offer no new complexity). Cube 7 has the most 1s and 0s.

	abcdefgh
1	111x100x
2	111x1x01
3	1100xx11
4	1100x1x1
5	00x10x10
6	00x1001x
7	00001x11
8	0000100x

and so it is chosen for factorization. Its product with 8,

7·8   00001xxx

has a maximum goodness. The next maximum product formed is of 5 and 6,

5·6   00x10x1x

then

1·2   111x1x0x

and then

3·4   1100xxx1.

Then

12·34   11xxxxxx and 56·78   00xxxxxx.

Factorization thus far yields

$$(ab(ce\overline{g}(\overline{f}+h) + \overline{cd}h(g+f)) + \overline{ab}\ (d\overline{e}g(\overline{f}+\overline{h}) + \overline{cde}\ (gh+\overline{fg}))$$

of "cost" (i.e. total gate inputs) 26. However, by combining cubes
3·4   1100xxx1 and 7·8   00001xxx in the second pass to form

$$xx00xxxx$$

the cost, by a "non-Boolean" implementation is reduced to 24, essentially by forming $q = \overline{cd}$ and substituting in the above expression. Fig.
2.8 depicts this implementation where · stands for A and + for Or.

2.9.   Implementation for LSI Logic Each technology comes with its
own logic primitives, with its own fan-in and fan-out limitations.
Before a logic design is complete, it is necessary that it be transformed
into one commensurate with specifications for one of these technologies. In LSI technologies the primitives are usually Nors or AIs together, respectively, with a special Or or And, called a dotted function,
which can be effected by the connection of the corresponding wires.
The transforms from abstract logic to a technology-dependent hardware design are heuristic and particularized for each technology. We
shall discuss a simple transformation for three technologies. A simple
function is expressed as the cube

$$abcd \mid uvw$$
$$1011 \mid 11x.$$

The first technology is supplied with a two-input And A and an Invert
N. In this case the logic can be realized in three levels as: $e=N(b)$;
$f=A(a,e)$; $g=A(c,d)$; $u=v=A(f,g)$; The second technology contains
only a two- and four-input And-Invert AI and a single N. Here a
three-level realization can also be obtained: $e=N(b)$; $f=AI(a,e,c,d)$;
$u=v=N(f)$; Finally, consider a technology containing the N plus the
four-input Or-Invert Nor (the Or followed by the N). Here the logic
can be realized in two levels: $u=v=Nor(N(a),b,N(c),N(d))$; this last
term is based upon DeMorgan's law (extended to four variables):

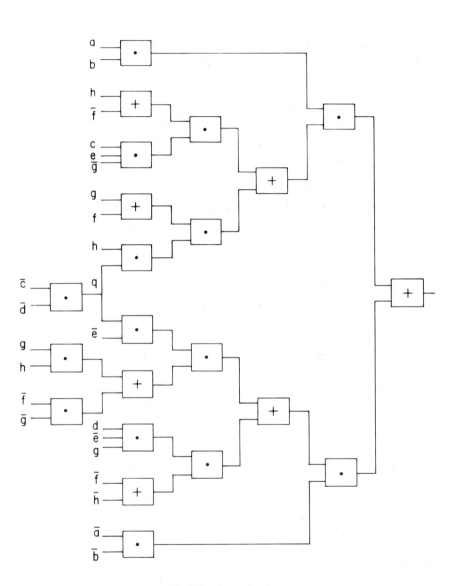

Fig. 2.8. Factorization

$A(a,b)=\text{Nor}(N(a),N(b))$; this may easily be verified by use of the #-product.

2.10. Automatic Logic. Detailed logic design is a time-consuming, error-prone task. One might examine the possibility of a high-level logic-design language plus a compiler as a means to eliminate this problem. In this chapter we introduce such means for acyclic designs. Later modifications necessary for a general design form will be made.

The R-notation was discussed in Chapter 1 as an algorithmic language. R-notation was easily employed to define logic. To find means for effecting a transformation of R-algorithms into logic designs, it was found expedient (1974, Halliwell-Roth) to define a (minuscule) subset PL/R of PL/I as a high-level language for logic design; Halliwell then defined a compiler RTRAN utilizing the PL/I optimizing compiler which transforms an algorithm written in PL/R into a regular logic design (cf. Chapter 4). It was originally designed so that the produced logic design was in the logic of a variety of technologies, at the user's option.

PL/R has only one data type, that of bit strings. The primitive logical functions in PL/R are NOT ¬, EQUALs =, AND &, OR |. DO loops can be used to facilitate expression of complicated designs. IF-THEN-ELSE instructions may be used. GOTOs are forbidden. Macros may be conveniently used to build up complex functions from simpler ones, and stored for future use. Only local optimization is used in RTRAN. It is fast, run-time growing about linearly with size of design. In one run on the IBM/360 model 91, for example, RTRAN produced a 2000 gate design in 20 seconds. For control logic that we chose RTRAN designs were comparable with those of skilled designers; for arithmetic and data flow, it was less successful.

We shall give a few PL/R designs in Chapter 5 together with their RTRAN implementations in the "pseudo-logic" of 2-input AIs and inverts N.

Incidentally the PL/R-RTRAN structure was built upon to produce an "R-compiler" accepting algorithms in R-notation, mapping them into "PL/R-algorithms" and then, via RTRAN, into logic (1974 Roth, Levy).

The principal use for RTRAN to date has been as a subsidiary program in verification (1977 Roth); cf. Chapter 6.

2.11. Other Work. Others have defined high-level logic-design languages such as DDL (for Digital Design Language) by Duley and Dietmeyer (1963); a translator into Boolean equations was subsequently written and used by a Japanese computer manufacturer for simulation purposes (1979 Dietmeyer).

Hu and Muroga have studied intensively the factorization problem for 4-input Nand and Nor networks (1977).

Preparata, Muller and Barak (1977) reduced the depth of "Boolean networks" and obtained bounds on computational complexity.

W. W. Peterson (1962) used programs based on the algorithm of Section 2.8, together with an early version of MIN370 (Chapter 1), to minimize error-correcting logic.

Problems

2.1. Realize the function of Fig. 2.3 with 2-input AIs.

2.2. Perform $P*$ to realize your design in Problem 2.1. Show equivalence with the cover of Fig. 2.3.

2.3. Perform $P*$ for Fig. 2.5 for the OFF-array (set $g=0$ and proceed).

2.4. Assure that the ON-array of Fig. 2.5 and your OFF-array of Problem 2.3 are disjoint.

2.5. Perform $P*$ on the design $j=\mathrm{MAJ}(h,d,i)$; $i=\mathrm{Xor}(e,f)$; $h=\mathrm{Xor}(g,c)$; $g=\mathrm{A}(a,b)$; where a, b, c, d, e, f are PIs. (Cf. Fig. 2.4).

Bibliography

1960. Roth, J. Paul, "Minimization over Boolean Trees," *IBM Journal of Research and Development*, vol. 4, pp. 543-558.

1962. Peterson, W. W., "Error-Correcting Codes", *The M.I.T. Press*, Cambridge, MA, and *John Wiley & Sons, Inc.*, NY.

1967. Schneider, P. R., "On the Necessity to Examine D-chains in Diagnostic Test Generation," *IBM Journal of Research and Development*, vol. 11, p. 114.

1968. Duley, James R. and Donald L. Dietmeyer, "A Digital System Design Language," *IEEE Transactions on Computers*, vol. C-17, pp. 850-861.

1974. Halliwell, H. & J. P. Roth, "System for Computer Design," *IBM Technical Disclosure Bulletin*, vol. 17, October, pp. 1517-1519.

1974. Roth, J. Paul & Leon S. Levy, "R-notation and its Usage in Computer Design", *Proceedings of 2nd Jerusalem Symposium on Information Technology*, pp. 589-603.

1977. Hu, K.C. and S. Muroga, "Nor Network Transduction System," Dept. of Computer Science, University of Illinois at Urbana-Champaign, UIUCDCS-R-77-885.

1977. Preparata, Franco P., David E. Muller and Ammon B. Barak, "Reduction of Depth of Boolean Networks with Fan-In Constraint," *IEEE Transactions on Computers* vol. C-26, pp. 474-479.

1978. Roth, J. Paul, "Hardware Verification," *IEEE Transactions on Computers*, vol. C-26, pp. 1294-96.

1979. Dietmeyer, Donald L. Personal communication.

Chapter 3

ACYCLIC TESTING

Introduction. We shall discuss here questions concerning the diagnosis of failures in acyclic logic designs as described in Chapter 2. In Chapter 5 we treat testing for the cyclic case. First we argue for the need for such testing.

3.1. Need for Testing. Computers may be composed from many thousands of primitive elements, sometimes called *circuits*, any of which may malfunction. Generally they are packaged in assemblages. Stimulus to and response from individual circuits are not in general available directly. Therefore the behavior of the individual circuits can be known only through the medium of other circuits and inputs and outputs, the I/Os, of the assemblages, usually in complex fashion. The testable assemblages are called *chips*, cards or modules.

Computers today have many critical missions, from medical to monetary. It is often essential to be able to diagnose reliably (and to repair) their failures. We begin, in this chapter, with the acyclic case.

A Logic Design L is any interconnection of primitives, logic blocks, here for the acyclic case, i.e., with the constraint that no feedback cycles be introduced. Primary Inputs PIs and Primary Outputs POs are designated. Arbitrary fan-in and -out are allowed. A *failure* F is a logical modification of L. Commonly F is assumed to be confined to a

single logic block. A *test* for F is a PI-pattern such that the resulting
PO-pattern differs depending on whether or not F is present.

Acyclic Failures. The *stuck* failure is most convenient to treat: any
block line, variable, may have its output fixed at 1 or 0. It is simple,
however, to treat failures of more "macro" portions of the design,
such failures being any change in the function of that portion. In
addition to the "stuck" failures, a pair of lines may become shorted,
introducing into the network a spurious logical A or Or, depending on
the technology. In this chapter all failures including the shorts are
acyclic.

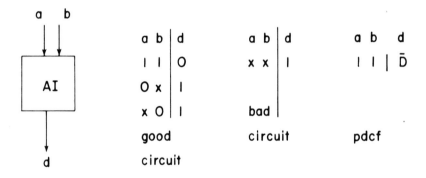

Fig. 3.1   Primitive D-cube of failure of an AI

Consider first failures of a logic primitive, a logic block, for
example, the 2-input Nand gate AI in Fig. 3.1, with inputs a, b and
output d. Its (singular) cover is given for the good circuit. Suppose
that output d becomes fixed, stuck at value 1. Then the cover of this
failing circuit is xx | 1.

Exercise: Find a cover of all input patterns yielding different outputs
for the good and failing circuits. Since the failing circuit is always 1 in

its output, all inputs for which the good machine is 0 will yield all such differing patterns. For this example, it is just 11 | 0.

3.2. D-notation. We wish to have a notation to capture the difference between the values assigned the relevant lines for the good and bad machine. Remember that in LSI technology it is not in general permissible to probe the output d of the AI under consideration (since it is assumed to be part of a much larger design). To test it, we must go through the intermediary of many other circuits in complex fashion, as we shall see.

First the notation must denote the difference in its operation between the correct and failing machine at the site of the failure. For example, in the failing AI described above, we write

$$11 \mid \overline{D}$$

to denote simultaneously 11 | 0 for the good and 11 | 1 for the bad the $\overline{D}$ standing both for 0 in the good, and 1 in the bad. 11 | $\overline{D}$ is termed a *primitive D-cube of failure pdcf:*   it represents two cubes and the discrepancy - D for Discrepancy - between operations of the two circuits.

A *pdcf* is formed from an input pattern to the circuit for which the correct circuit has the value 1 and the incorrect, 0:   in this case the output has the value D; if the opposite, $\overline{D}$.

Let us now incorporate the AI of Fig. 3.1 into a larger design MAJ, a 3-input majority, as shown in Fig. 3.2.

Assume failure in line d. Again, we are not able to probe the line d directly: it is inaccessible to the exterior of the design, the chip. What we must do is to drive the difference D down to the primary output m.   This must be done through a number of assignments of values to various lines of the design.

Now d feeds only the circuit with output g and we must allow the changes of d to propagate through to g. If e, the other input to g, has the value 0 then g will assume the value 1 *regardless* of the value of d. If on the other hand e is assigned the value 1, then the value on d will be inverted on g: when $d=1$ then $g=0$; $d=0$ implies $g=1$. We thus assign 1 to e and to g the symbol D. We call the connected subset of d and g together with their values $d = \overline{D}$; $g=D$ a *D-chain*. Also assumed by the D-chain are the other assignments, $a=1$, $b=1$, $e=1$, necessary for the existence of this D-chain.

In general a *D-chain* consists of a consistent assignment to each line of a subset of a logical design one of the five values $0,1,x,D,\overline{D}$.

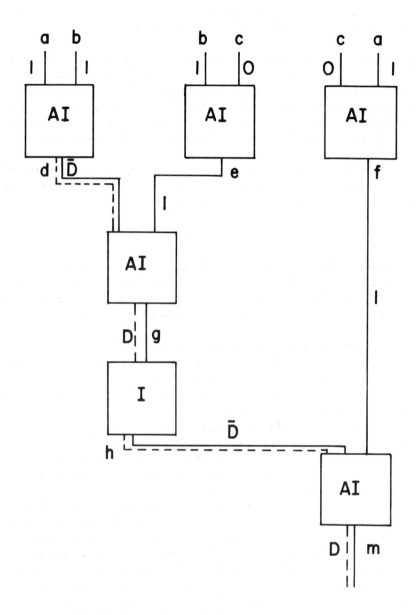

Fig. 3.2. Computing test for failure in majority circuit

Such a *D*-chain on a subset can always be extended to the entire logic design by the simple expedient of assigning x to each unassigned line. Whereas the xs of a *D*-chain, *D*-cube, may take on arbitrary values independently of each other, the *D*s and $\overline{D}$s are dependent, defining only two patterns, for the case when all *D*s equal 1 and $\overline{D}$s equal 0 and vice versa.

Primitive *D*-cubes: The values assigned to *g* and its inputs *d,e* are termed *primitive D-cubes pdc*s. These are necessary in our method to compute the full test for failure. We shall compute them *ab initio* from the cover of Fig. 3.1.

The *primitive D-cube pdc* specifies conditions on all but one or more selected inputs of a block so as to guarantee transmission of a change in the selected inputs into a change in the output.

Any two singular cubes of a circuit determine a *pdc* of the circuit: if the coordinate interface of the two cubes has a common value 0, 1 or x, the corresponding coordinate of the *pdc* has this value; if the coordinate of the first cube is 1 and the second 0 the *pdc* has *D* for this coordinate; if the opposite, $\overline{D}$.

D-interface. We define *D-interface* at this point: it is used in an essential manner in generating a test from *pdc*s and *pdcf*s of a failing logic circuit. Let $a = (a1,...,an)$ and $b = (b1,...,bn)$ be *D*-cubes where each *ai* and *bi* is equal to 0,1,x,*D*, or $\overline{D}$. Then coordinate *D*-interface *J* is defined by the following rules:

1)   x *J* *ai* = *ai* *J* x = *ai*

2)   if *ai*≠x and *bi*≠x then

$$ai \; J \; bi \; = \; \begin{cases} ai \text{ if } bi=ai \\ \phi \text{ otherwise} \end{cases}$$

where ϕ stands for the empty set. Then $a \; J \; b \; = \; \phi$ if for any *i*, *ai* *J* *bi* = ϕ Otherwise the *D*-interface of cubes is defined as

$$a \; J \; b \; = \; (a1 \; J \; b1,...,an \; J \; bn).$$

For example $01xDx \; J \quad 0x1D\overline{D}=011D\overline{D}$ and $01xDx \; J \; 00x1D\overline{D}=\phi$.

3.3. **Test Generation.** Continuing with test generation, for Fig. 3.2, by performing the D-interface defined above, of

$$
\begin{array}{ccc}
a & b & d \\
1 & 1 & \overline{D}
\end{array}
$$

with

$$
\begin{array}{ccc}
d & e & g \\
\overline{D} & 1 & D
\end{array}
$$

we obtain the D-chain

$$
\begin{array}{ccccc}
a & b & d & e & g \\
1 & 1 & \overline{D} & 1 & D
\end{array}
$$

The D-frontier of the D-chain, all blocks whose inputs contain a D or $\overline{D}$ and whose output is x, unspecified, is h only. It therefore is "driven" through its successor block h. Now h, as an invert function, has the cover

$$
\begin{array}{cc}
g & h \\
1 & 0 \\
0 & 1
\end{array}
$$

Its *pdc* is

$$
\begin{array}{cc}
g & h \\
D & \overline{D}
\end{array}
$$

Interfacing with the developing D-chain

$$
\begin{array}{ccccc}
a & b & d & e & g \\
1 & 1 & \overline{D} & 1 & D,
\end{array}
$$

we obtain

$$
\begin{array}{cccccc}
a & b & d & e & g & h \\
1 & 1 & \overline{D} & 1 & D & \overline{D},
\end{array}
$$

whose D-frontier is h, whose relevant *pdc* is

$$f \quad h \quad m$$
$$1 \quad \overline{D} \quad D$$

Its D-interface with the above D-chain yields

$$a \quad b \qquad d \quad e \quad f \quad g \quad h \quad m$$
$$1 \quad 1 \qquad \overline{D} \quad 1 \quad 1 \quad D \quad \overline{D} \quad D$$

and the primary output is reached. This D-cube does not yet, however, completely define a test for the failure d stuck-at-1, since values assigned to internal lines, $e = f = 1$, must be *justified* in terms of values on primary inputs. Thus for this purpose we inspect their covers, all identical to that of the good circuit of Fig. 3.1. We see from the cover

$$
\begin{array}{ccc}
b & c & e \\
1 & 1 & 0 \\
0 & x & 1 \\
x & 0 & 1
\end{array}
$$

that to get a 1 on e we must use either of the last two cubes. But 0x1 conflicts with

$$a \quad b \qquad d \quad e \quad f \quad g \quad h \quad m$$
$$1 \quad 1 \qquad \overline{D} \quad 1 \quad 1 \quad D \quad \overline{D} \quad D$$

in its b-coordinate. But using the third, x01, we get

$$\qquad\qquad a \quad b \quad c \quad d \quad e \quad f \quad g \quad h \quad m$$
$$tc = \qquad 1 \quad 1 \quad 0 \quad D \quad 1 \quad 1 \quad \overline{D} \quad D \quad \overline{D}$$

Note that this last assignment automatically assigned a singular cube 101 to e as well.

This D-chain that we developed specifies primary input pattern 110 for input variables a, b, c which detects the failure d stuck-at-1 at the PO m; if no failure occurs under this input pattern, $m = 1$; if this failure occurs, then m will be 0. Values on all lines 1, 0, x, D or $\overline{D}$, for good and bad machines at any stage of the computation, are determined by the *test cube tc*.

3.4 The D-algorithm, by Example. The first part of the algorithm, called the *D-algorithm,* is termed *D-drive*. The last, assigning values to primary inputs in order to assure the maintenance of values on internal lines assigned during *D*-drive, is termed CONSISTENCY.

Let us work a few more illustrative examples. The following example, Fig. 3.3, is complicated by the fact that the logic primitives are And, Or, Xor, Not, as well as AI. The covers for each primitive, together with the necessary primitive *D*-cubes, *pdc*s, are given in Fig. 3.3. We assume a failure on line 1 as stuck at 0, so that a *D* is imposed on line 1. The *D*-frontier of this tiny *D*-chain consists of lines (blocks) 5 and 8. We may choose either of these through which to

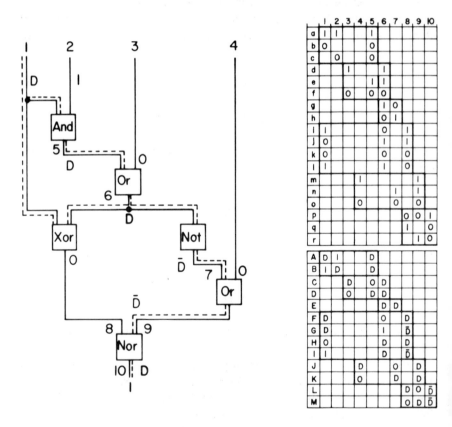

Fig. 3.3. A circuit, its cover and primitive *D*-cubes for the *D*-algorithm

D-drive and, in the complete *D*-algorithm, if one choice fails the other
will be examined later. Let us choose line 5. From the *D*-cube table
we see that the *pdc* $D1D$ on lines 1,2,5 respectively is needed. Thus
the test cube *tc* being developed at this stage amounts to $D1D$ on lines
1, 2, 5.

The new *D*-frontier is 6 and 8. We choose line 6, a 2-input Or.
We choose for its *pdc*

$$3\ \ 5\ \ 6$$
$$0\ \ D\ \ D$$

Its *D*-interface, with *tc* equal to $D1D$ on lines 1, 2, 5 yields the new

$$\begin{array}{cccccc} 1 & 2 & 3 & 5 & 6 \\ tc = & D & 1 & 0 & D & D \end{array}$$

We may now take two implications of *tc* as currently constituted. First
consider line 8, the Xor block. Its input coordinates in *tc* are DD,
covering input patterns 11 and 00, the output for both being 0. It
follows that the appropriate *pdc* is $DD0$ on lines 1,6,8. Next, on the
D-frontier is line 7 which is a Not function. Its input in *tc* is D. Therefore its output - see Table - must be $\overline{D}$. Thus with corresponding
D-interfaces *tc* becomes

$$\begin{array}{ccccccc} 1 & 2 & 3 & 5 & 6 & 7 & 8 \\ D & 1 & 0 & D & D & \overline{D} & 0 \end{array}$$

The new *D*-frontier is 9. To pursue *D*-drive through 9 we select
the *pdc* $0\ \overline{D}\ \overline{D}$, in coordinates 4, 7, 9 (9 being an Or) and *D*-interface,
to form

$$\begin{array}{ccccccccc} 1 & 2 & 3 & 4 & 5 & 6 & 7 & 8 & 9 \\ tc = & D & 1 & 0 & 0 & D & D & \overline{D} & 0 & \overline{D} \end{array}$$

Finally 10 is the new *D*-frontier. With a $\overline{D}$ on input line 9, one
selects for this Nor block the *pdc* $0\overline{D}D$. Its *D*-interface with the current *tc* yields the final *D*-chain

$$\begin{array}{cccccccccc} 1 & 2 & 3 & 4 & 5 & 6 & 7 & 8 & 9 & 10 \\ tc = & D & 1 & 0 & 0 & D & D & \overline{D} & 0 & \overline{D} & D \end{array}$$

The values of the first four coordinates of tc determine the test in terms of Primary Input PI patterns. On the good machine $D = 1$, so that the PI pattern is

$$
\begin{array}{cccc}
1 & 2 & 3 & 4 \\
1 & 1 & 0 & 0.
\end{array}
$$

When this pattern is applied, then the output 10 has the value 1 if the failure is absent and 0 if it is present. The test cube tc above is termed the *D-cube of test T and failure F* and is denoted $c(T,F)$.

Outline of D-algorithm. A failure is assumed in one of the circuits of the acyclic design. A *pdcf* for it is selected. *D*-drive is executed, to cause a change, D or $\bar{D}$, to be manifested at a PO depending upon the presence or absence of this failure, manifested at a PO (by segmentation only one PO may be assumed); *D*-drive is accomplished by selecting appropriate *pdc*s of blocks on the *D*-frontier of the developing test cube tc and *D*-interfacing them with the developing tc; if a nonempty interface is achieved the new tc is specified to be this interface; if an empty interface is achieved, another *pdc* is assumed for the particular block on the *D*-frontier unless no such *pdc*s remain in which case one returns, in recursive fashion, to the last choice of *pdc* in tc formation, etc. At each successful choice all possible implications are made; upon the tc reaching the PO, CONSISTENCY is executed consisting of interfacing "backwards" the tc with appropriate cubes of blocks with a 1 or 0 as coordinates in the tc; ultimately there is obtained a tc having PI coordinates specifying a test cube for the given failure, in general having values 0, 1, x, D, $\bar{D}$.

Exercise. CONSISTENCY played a rudimentary role in the above calculation. Suppose now that 3 is the output of a Nor block with inputs a,b. Thus the PIs are $1,2,a,b,4$. Apply CONSISTENCY for this case for the same failure.

We now consider a circuit due essentially to Peter R. Schneider (1967) illustrating another aspect of the *D*-algorithm. In Fig. 3.4 we have seven 2-input AIs together with one 4-input AI connected as shown.

A *sensitive path* is a simple *D*-chain from site of failure to a primary output. Several test-generating algorithms attempt to generate a test based solely upon sensitive paths. The following example shows

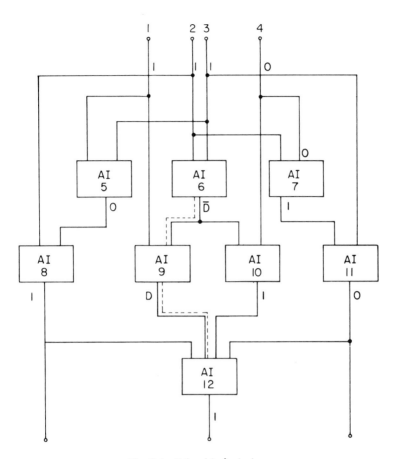

Fig. 3.4. Schneider's design

that a sensitive path is not sufficient: in general a "multiple *D*-chain" is required.

Consider the failure of line 6 stuck at 1.   In order to test this failure it is necessary to impose the signal 1 on lines 2 and 3, inputs to 6. Equivalently, we start with *pdcf* 11$\overline{D}$. Suppose first that we require the sensitive path to go through block 9.

If the *D*-chain is to be simple, since it passes through block 9, it may not pass through block 10. The only way for this to occur is for line 4 to be 0 (allowing line 10 to be 1 independently of the value $\overline{D}$ of its other input). Because the input to block 7 is 1, 0 its output is 1 (cf. Fig. 3.4); hence because the input to 11 is 1,1 its output is 0, preventing the D-chain on line 9 from going through block 12. Hence no sensitive-path test exists for this failure.

Exercise. Compute a test for line 6 stuck at 1 in Fig. 3.4 by the D-algorithm. Depict this "double" D-chain on a sketch of the circuit.

We shall return to the D-algorithm in Chapter 5 where we consider its adaptation to the cyclic case. The D-algorithm has been widely used, specifically by IBM (1977).

3.5. Optimized D-algorithm. In the original D-algorithm (1966) the computation of a test-for-failure proceeds in two stages: first the D-drive from the site of failure to the primary output; next CONSISTENCY, reasoning backwards to the PIs. In the 1967 version of the program, "plunges" to the output were made to speed up the process. Here at each stage we compute the D-*frontier* - circuits with an x on their output and a D or $\overline{D}$ on their inputs - and the C-*frontier* - circuits having 0,1,D or $\overline{D}$ as output, but whose input is not yet determined. We say that a circuit is "on the frontier" if it is on the D-frontier or C-frontier. If a circuit is on the D-frontier, its "distance" is measured in terms of the number of circuits to the PO. Similarly the distance to the PIs for members of the C-frontier is measured. That circuit with the smallest such distance, whether on the D-frontier or C-frontier, is chosen for extension of the D-chain. Thus if such a circuit - there may be more than one - is on the C-frontier, then it will be extended backwards; if on the D-frontier, forwards. Of course at each step, all possible implications are taken.

It is estimated, based on the relative performance of a program giving priority to backward extensions of the D-chain alone, that this "optimized" version will be at least 50 percent faster than the original version; cf. 1978 Roth.

3.6. TESTDETECT. It is one task to compute a test to detect some given failure in a logic design. Usually, however, it is desired to compute a set of tests to detect any of a prescribed set of failures. A common set of failures are all stuck-at-1 and stuck-at-0 failures, for each primitive in the design. One test is generally insufficient to cover all failures and it is then necessary to compute more than one test. In this process of computation of a test-set to cover a failure-set, it is convenient to be able to determine all failures that a given test detects. One technique to find all failures detected by a given test is to *simulate* the behavior of the design, once for each failure. We shall describe TESTDETECT which is considerably faster than simulation. It does the computation essentially once, for all failures. It is described here for stuck failures only.

We use TESTDETECT in obtaining a covering set of tests: first by computing a test by the D-algorithm for a selected failure; using TESTDETECT to eliminate from the "running" all failures detected by this test; choosing an untested failure; computing by the D-algorithm a new test for it, etc.

Again there is no loss of generality to assume that the design has just one output. We use SEGMENT to subdivide it so. The sum of running times for the segments will be substantially less than that for the unsegmented original.

Consider Fig. 3.3 above with the input pattern 1101. First we compute the signal on every line in the design for this input pattern. This is 1 1 0 1 1 1 0 0 1 0 for lines 1 through 10. We then start our computation of failures detected by this input pattern, beginning at PO 10 and working backward therefrom.

Since 10 has the value 0, it is tested for stuck at 1. (POs are always tested). On line 10 we therefore place the designation FD, for failure detected.

Consider now line 9. Is it detected by this same test? First we find out in a direct way. Note that for any test T and failure F we define a *test cube of test and failure*,

$$c = c(T, F),$$

according to the rules: For line i if both good and bad circuits have signal s, then $c(i) = s$; if the good has a 1 and the bad a 0 then $c(i) = D$; if the reverse, $c(i) = \overline{D}$.

Let us construct c for $T = 1101$ and for an appropriate stuck failure on line 9:

$$
\begin{array}{cccccccccc}
 & 1 & 2 & 3 & 4 & 5 & 6 & 7 & 8 & 9 & 10 \\
c(T,9) = & 1 & 1 & 0 & 1 & 1 & 1 & 0 & 0 & D & 1
\end{array}
$$

With this test, the D-chain emanating from 9 does not reach PO 10, for the 0 on line 8 kills it off. On the other hand the failure   line 8 stuck at 1 is detected, for

$$c(T,8) = \begin{array}{cccccccccc} 1 & 2 & 3 & 4 & 5 & 6 & 7 & 8 & 9 & 10 \\ 1 & 1 & 0 & 1 & 1 & 1 & 0 & \overline{D} & 1 & D \end{array}$$

Exercise. Construct $c(T,F)$ for each appropriate stuck failure in the circuit of Fig. 3.3.

Thus *one method* for finding all Fs detected by a given T is to construct their corresponding $c(T,F)$s. TESTDETECT is an abridgement of this method. SEGMENT is first used to reduce multiple output designs to several equivalent single-output problems. The computation then starts with the PO, to determine how that is tested by test T. It works progressively back through the circuit and utilizes previous computations to truncate subsequent ones.

The general idea of TESTDETECT is to compute, for any failure F and test T, the test cube $c(T,F)$ only to the extent necessary to determine the fate of F under T by use of prior such calculations for all failures closer to the Primary Output.

We make the TESTDETECT computations for Fig. 3.3 with PI pattern 1101. Reviewing, PO 10 is tested for the failure stuck at 0. A $\overline{D}$ emanating from 9 is immediately killed off by the 0 on line 8: with 8 having value 0 the PO will have value 1 *regardless* of the value on 9. Hence 9 is undetected by test 1101. Continuing, line 8 is tested since its D-chain, because 9 has value 1, impinges on 10 and no other line, and 10 is itself tested.

Moving back in the network, we see that 7 is undetected since the other input 4 to the Or which 7 feeds is 1, killing off the D-chain from 7. For 9 is then 1 regardless of the value of 7.

Consider now block 6. The D-chain from 6 to block 7 dies because that from 7 dies. But that feeding 8 is testable since it arrives at 8, with the other input 1 being 1. The D-chain from 6 has been reduced to a single line, 8. Thus - see lemma below - 6 is testable if and only if 8 is testable. Hence, with no further computations, we say that 6 is detected by 1101, specifically for stuck-at-0. Likewise line 5 is detected since the other input to the Or, which it feeds, is 0, allowing 5's D-chain to arrive at 6 which we have seen is detected by application of the same lemma: 5 is detected if and only if 6 is detected.

The D-chain from 4 reduces to line 9, which we computed to be undetected. Hence 4 is not detected. Box 3 is undetected since its incipient D-chain is killed off by 5's being 1, both 5 and 3 feeding an Or. But 2's D-chain reduces to the single detected line 6. Hence 2 is detected. The computation for 1 is the most interesting. The D-chain from 1 fans out to 5, and 8. Since 1 and 6 feed an Xor, the D-chain impinging there terminates, for its output 8 will be 0 regardless of failure on line 1. The portion impinging on block 9 also terminates because of the 1 on line 4. Thus the stuck failures on line 1 are undetected by 1101.

Exercise. Apply TESTDETECT to the design of Fig. 3.4 with inputs 1001 and others.

Exercise: Determine the fate of all lines for test 1000 in Fig. 3.3.

The lemma which makes this truncation process work goes as follows:

Lemma. If, at any stage in the computation of $c(T,F)$ for test T and (stuck) failure F, the D-frontier reduces to a single line l and if there is no reconvergent fanout beyond the D-frontier, then F is testable if and only if l is testable. (See 1969.)

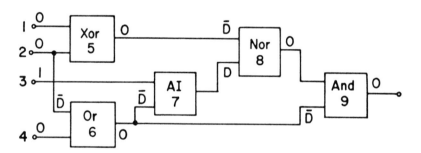

Fig. 3.5 Design demonstrating need for a reconvergence condition

The example of Fig. 3.5 illustrates the need for some reconvergence condition such as stated by the lemma. Here the D-chain emanating from line 2 reduces to a D on line 6, which is testable. On the other hand the D-chain from line 2 reconverges; one branch is eliminated at block 8, with $D\overline{D}$ inputs; this presents block 9 with inputs $0\overline{D}$, yielding a 0 on the PO, so that 2 is *not* detected even though 6 is, and the D-chain from 2 reduces to 6. See 1969.

3.7.   *D*-algorithm Used with TESTDETECT.   Assume what is needed is a set of tests to detect any of a set of failures. Typically the set of failures consists of all stuck failures. On the other hand a program at the IBM T. J. Watson Research Center includes also any set of shorts specified by the user. The program determines whether or not feedback was introduced by the short. If there was it would be rejected as untestable. If not, it would be processed after the stuck failures.

One strategy is first to: select a failure of a primary input; use the D-algorithm to compute a test for it; then use TESTDETECT to find all failures detected by this given test; delete them from the list of untested failures; seek another as yet untested failure at the shortest distance to the PIs as possible, etc., until all failures are tested.

3.8.   Validity of the *D*-algorithm.   A proof (1966) has been given of the validity of the D-algorithm: given a failure in an acyclic logic design, the D-algorithm will compute a test to detect it if such a test exists. The proof starts with an assumed test T for a failure F. It constructs the D-cube $c(T,F)$ of test and failure, consisting of, for each line: the signal imposed by T on the correct design if the failing design agrees with it; D if the signal is 1 in the "good" and 0 in the "bad"; $\overline{D}$, if the reverse. It then uses lemmas to show that, for each such line or logic block in the design, a singular cube, primitive D-cube or primitive D-cube of failure, contains $c(T,F)$. Hence, by one of the lemmas, the D-interface of all these contains $c(T,F)$. Finally it shows that the sequencing of the D-algorithm yields a test cube $c(T^*,F)$ for some test T^* (not necessarily the same as T). Since $c(T^*,F)$ uniquely determines T^*, the theorem is proved. Cf. 1966 for a complete proof.

Programs.   Two programming implementations of the D-algorithm in conjunction with TESTDETECT were made at the IBM T. J. Watson Research Center. The first was written in APL largely by P. R. Schneider. The programs were published in 1967, (Roth, Bouricius, Schneider). A new version of TESTDETECT with the reconvergence condition appeared in 1969. The second program was written in 1972 by H. Halliwell in PL/I.   Since it handled cyclic (sequential) logic, discussion will be deferred to Chapter 5.   It could handle on the order of 1000 circuits.

The output form for TESTDETECT 1967 was especially convenient for the user.   Fig. 3.6 depicts this for a logic circuit consisting of seven logic blocks connected as shown.

Below the diagram is the form of the output.   The first four columns, corresponding to the four PIs, for each row give a PI-pattern. The columns following in the same row correspond to each of the 11 lines in the design.   In each of these columns a 1 appears if the PI-pattern detects a stuck-at-1 failure on this line.   Similarly a 0 means that the test detects a stuck-at-0 failure on this line.   A blank indicates that the test detects no stuck failure on this line.

Fig. 3.7 shows a computation for Fig. 3.4.   Note that there is only one test for line 6 stuck-at-1.   No sensitive paths exist!   This means, as Schneider showed, that there is no test for this failure which would correspond to a sensitive path, a linear chain of Ds and $\overline{D}$s.

3.9 Delay Testing.   Each circuit requires a certain time, measured say in nanoseconds, to respond to a change in its input configuration. Along some path from primary input to primary output, there will also be experienced a delay being, to the first approximation, the sum of the delays of the circuits composing it.   These delays, both circuit and path, may vary, with circuit and with time.   A stuck failure in fact might be considered a "delay failure" for a very long delay.

Suppose that a circuit in an acyclic piece (cyclic case considered in Chapter 5) of logic acquires an unacceptably large delay.

Problem: Find a test sequence which detects this delay failure.

Assume that the large delay is from the transfer from 0(1) to 1(0).   To develop a test we require a sequence of PI patterns of length 2; in the first, to impose a signal 0(1), in the second, 1(0).

Imagine therefore that we have two copies of the design, one for each input pattern.   We start, as in this chapter, with a D on the output of the failing circuit and we select, as per the D-algorithm, a $pdcf$ to go along with it.

Now, as in the classical D-algorithm, we wish to D-drive to a PO and with segmentation we can assume this to be a single output but we wish to take it along the longest possible route.

For this purpose we use the algorithm DELAY described in Section 4.6 of Chapter 4 to order the elements, at each stage of the

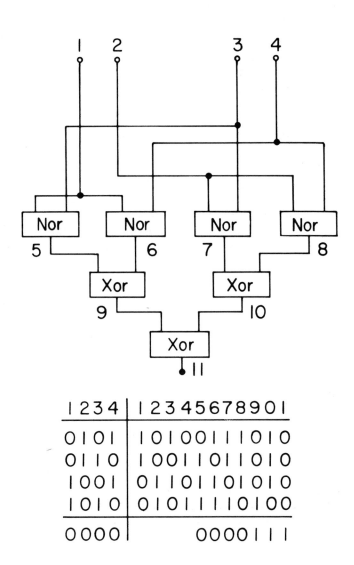

1 2 3 4	1 2 3 4 5 6 7 8 9 0 1
0 1 0 1	1 0 1 0 0 1 1 1 0 1 0
0 1 1 0	1 0 0 1 1 0 1 1 0 1 0
1 0 0 1	0 1 1 0 1 1 0 1 0 1 0
1 0 1 0	0 1 0 1 1 1 1 0 1 0 0
0 0 0 0	0 0 0 0 1 1 1

Fig. 3.6. Output for TESTDETECT

computation, on the D-frontier of the D-chain, and we select these elements in descending order of delay.

Then in the CONSISTENCY algorithm we do the same thing for driving back: for the C-frontier, we select according to longest delay.   For the first pattern we perform a simplified form of CONSISTENCY (no Ds or $\bar{D}$s) to obtain the desired signal.   Cf. 1974, Roth.

DETECT

```
                    111
 1234| 123456789012
-----+---------------
 0000|1111    00001
 0001| 110 0 0 100
 0010| 10    00  10
 0011| 10    00  10
 0100| 01 0  1  00
 0101| 0  0  1  00
 0110| 10010 01  10
 0111| 10 00 11  00
 1000|011  0 01 00
 1001| 11  0 0  00
 1010| 0    00  10
 1011| 10    00  10
 1100| 01 0  1  00
 1101| 01 0  1  00
 1110|0 011 00  10
 1111|000011100001
```

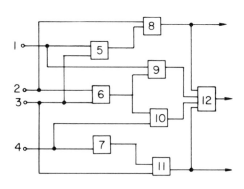

Fig. 3.7. TESTDETECT example

Computing a Test Assemblage. In testing logic such as on a chip or module, one is given an assemblage A of failures possibly described by formula. An example of such an assemblage would be the set of all "stuck" failures plus certain short failures as determined algorithmically by layout considerations. One needs therefore an assemblage of tests to detect, collectively, all the failures in A. One effective heuristic is the following:

1) Select a failure F by some procedure such as nearness to primary inputs.

2) Use the D-algorithm to compute test T to detect F.

3) Use TESTDETECT to determine all failures $D(T)$ of A detected by T.

4) if $A2=A-D(T)$ is not empty return to 1), with $A2$ substituted for A.

Continue until a set T of such tests covering A is obtained. D. B. Armstrong (1970) recommended the heuristic in 1). More sophisticated procedures can be used (1975).

3.10. Distinguishing Failures. We have discussed the D-algorithm to compute a test to detect any given failure. A test will in general detect many failures, however, and for purposes of repair it is necessary to identify just which failure has occurred, at least up to indistinguishable elements in equivalence classes. In this section we extend the D-algorithm to *distinguish* between any two distinguishable failures.

Let A and B denote two failures in a logic design and suppose that it is desired to compute a test to distinguish between them. Clearly a necessary condition is that either one of them, say A, must yield a response under test T that is different from that of the perfect circuit. Accordingly we use the D-algorithm, appropriately modified, to compute a test that will distinguish the logic circuit with failure A from the perfect logic circuit and at the same time distinguish A from B. If this is not possible, we reverse the roles of A and B. If neither is possible, then A and B are indistinguishable. The procedure checks at each stage of the extension of the developing test cube tc, for failure A, whether or not the distinguishing signals D and E from A and B respectively are themselves mutually distinguishable. Thus in general it is not necessary to go through the algorithm exhaustively to ascertain that no distinguishing test exists: it will ordinarily be so determined *in media res*.

The Iterative Method. We assume the failures A and B are on distinct lines. Thus the initial D-chain *tc* and E-chain *te* are disjoint for A and B respectively. Thus in extending these chains we need to come to terms with the case when line k has for its input lines i and j, $tci = D$ or $\overline{D}$ and $tej = E$ or $\overline{E}$. We shall discuss the case of 2-input And- and Or-blocks, with no loss of generality. Since the occurrences of failures A and B are mutually exclusive, when $D = 0$ (A has failed) then $E = 1$ (B has not failed) and vice versa. Thus if the block is an Or, the output is identically 1; if an And, identically 0. Hence the output $tck = tek = 0$ or 1 depending upon whether the block is an And or an Or. Clearly the same result holds when $tci=\overline{D}$ and $tej=\overline{E}$.

Now consider the case when $tci = D$ and $tej = \overline{E}$. For this purpose suppose that neither failure has occurred. Then $tci = D = 1$ and $tej = \overline{E} = 0$ so that output on line k is a 0 for the block A. Let us compare this with the case when failure A has occurred but B has not. Then $D = 0$ and $\overline{E} = 0$, so that the output for the And-block will also be zero, so that tck should be 0. For the case in which A has not failed but B has, output k is 1 so that $tek = \overline{E}$. Hence for this case the D-chain *tc* does not propagate through to line k, but the E-chain *te* does. In similar fashion if the block were an Or, tck would be D and $tek = 1$. It is easy to extend this analysis to arbitrary logic blocks.

Lemma. In logic circuit L subject to failure A or failure B but not both, suppose that, corresponding to any input pattern T, the value on some line l is fixed, i.e., $tc(l) = i = 1$ or 0. Then it is not possible that $te(l) = E$ or $\overline{E}$. Specifically it is necessary that $te(l) = i$.

Proof. To have the fixed value i means that it assumes this value independently of whether failure A occurs or not, i.e. $D = 1$ or 0. But since failures A and B are mutually exclusive and mutually exhaustive, the value E (or $\overline{E}$) clearly changes, dependent upon this circumstance. Hence the signal on line l cannot be constant. Q.E.D.

Note that in the above lemma it is not necessary that the input pattern T be assumed to be a primary input pattern. Thus these criteria will be used in the D-algorithm so modified at each stage of extension of the D-chain: if a line has inputs D or $\overline{D}$ and E or $\overline{E}$, then its own signal will be determined according to the above and, in any event, it will be removed from the D-frontier of the developing tc.

If on the other hand $tc(l) = 1$ or 0 and $te(l) = E$ or $\overline{E}$, this is a contradiction and the last decision prior to this circumstance must accordingly be undone or if there remain no subsequent alternate choices, then the quest for a distinguishing test will be terminated as unsuccessful.

3.11 Description of Distinguishing Algorithm. First it will be attempted to compute a test distinguishing between A and B for which the output pattern for failure A is different from that of the perfect circuit. If this is not possible then a distinguishing test is sought for which the failure pattern of B is different from that of the perfect circuit. If neither is possible then no test exists distinguishing between A and B.

The algorithm then begins with the imposition of a D on the line manifesting failure A:

$$tc(0) \;=\; \begin{array}{c} A \\ D \end{array}$$

we do not start out with a $pdcf$ - unless there is only one $pdcf$ - but instead merely impose D on the appropriate line and then at a later time, in CONSISTENCY, select an appropriate $pdcf$. (This procedure will in general be more efficient.) At each stage of development of the test cube tc corresponding to failure A we compute the corresponding implie; development of the test cube te for failure B.

Having developed the test cubes for failures A and B up to the nth step, $tc(n)$ and $te(n)$, we select for the line l appropriately chosen from the D-frontier of $tc(n)$ a pdc and D-interface it with $tc(n)$, to form

$$tc^*(n+1) \;=\; tc(n) \; J \; pdc.$$

If this D-interface is empty, we proceed as in the D-algorithm to another choice of pdc replacing the present one, or to another D-frontier line l if no other pdcs are available. If this interface is nonempty then all possible implications of this change are made, to form $tc(n+1)$. Then all possible corresponding implications of this change are made on $te(n)$, to form $te(n+1)$. Then any possible conflicts are ascertained between (the new parts of) $tc(n+1)$ and $te(n+1)$ as in the above lemma. If any conflicts occur the development is restored to the last decision point (lemma above). If $D(\overline{D})$ and $E(\overline{E})$

occur on the inputs to a given line k, tck and tek are computed by the iterative method. Then the procedure continues inductively until the D-chain from A reaches a primary output.

Thence one goes through the CONSISTENCY operation to complete the development of a test cube tc for failure A; at each stage the implied development of the test cube te for failure B is made and inconsistencies between these two are checked as above. It is clear that for any primary input coordinate of the final tc that is x, any choice may be made without a conflict arising between tc and te.

This completes the description of the distinguishing algorithm. We must now prove the effectiveness of the algorithm.

Theorem.   Given failures A and B in a logic circuit L, the distinguishing algorithm will compute a test distinguishing them if such a test exists.

Proof.   The proof is very similar to that for the D-algorithm and is modelled after it. Let T be a distinguishing test and $c(T,A)$ and $c(T,B)$ be the D-cubes of test T and failures A and B respectively; as above, however, assume that the response of A to test T is different from that of the perfect circuit and thus that there is a connected D-chain from A to some primary output which is not also reached by the E-chain emanating from B. The distinguishing algorithm, as with the D-algorithm, establishes a lexicographical ordering of D-chains, the order of formation by the algorithm itself; let it be assumed that the algorithm forms no D-chain defining a distinguishing test T^* before constructing $c(T,A)$ and $c(T,B)$, for otherwise the theorem is already proved.

We start out with a D on the line corresponding to failure A, $tc(0) = D$. The algorithm selects a line on the D-frontier of $tc(0)$ and selects a *pdc p* therefor; if this line and *pdc* does not correspond to that of $c(T,A)$, this means that this choice would run into a "blind alley" for by hypothesis there is no $c(T^*,A)$, $T^* \neq T$, constructed by the algorithm before $c(T,A)$. Therefore we choose the *pdc p* defined by $c(T,A)$ and form the D-interface

$$tc^*(1) = tc(0) \, J \, p$$

Since both $tc(0)$ and p D-contain $c(T,A)$, so does their D-interface and their interface is thus nonempty, by Lemma 5 of 1966. Likewise the D-interface $tc(1)$, derived from $tc^*(1)$, D-contains $tc^*(1)$ and $c(T,A)$, for the same implications of $tc(1)$ would also be made by $c(T,A)$. Likewise we form the E-chain $te(1)$, implied by $tc(1)$, emanating from the failure B. Clearly $te(1)$ contains $c(T,B)$ since $te(1)$ is implied by $tc^*(1)$ which is only a part of $c(T,A)$.

Suppose then that $tc(n)$ containing $c(T,A)$ and $te(n)$ containing $c(T,B)$ have been formed. Let p be the primitive D-cube or primitive singular cube next selected by the algorithm; it may be assumed that p contains $c(T,A)$ since by hypothesis all test cubes constructed in lexicographical order before $c(T,A)$ fail. Thus their D-interface

$$tc^*(n+1) = tc(n) \; J \; p$$

also D-contains $c(T,A)$ as well as $tc(n+1)$, the result of all implications from $tc^*(n+1)$. Likewise we form $te(n+1)$ as a result of $te(n)$ and the new implications from $tc(n+1)$; as a result of this by the above Lemma and the interactive method, certain members of the D-frontier may possibly be eliminated. Thus the distinguishing algorithm proceeds inductively until the test cube tc for failure is justified in terms of primary input patterns. Furthermore this pattern T^*, being in general a cube (i.e. having some x-coordinates) will contain T and will by construction distinguish A from B. Q.E.D.

Efficiency of Algorithm. It is estimated that the time to compute a test distinguishing between two failures will be somewhat longer than although of the same order of magnitude as for the D-algorithm to compute a test to detect any given failure. For there are only a few extra operations in the distinguishing algorithm over the D-algorithm in the basic operation of extending the D-chain by D-intersection. I would estimate the distinguishing algorithm executes half as fast as the D-algorithm.

3.12 Other Work. Armstrong (1972) has proposed another method of failure simulation: essentially it propagates forward D's from all related failures. Storage can be a problem. Cf., also its extension to functional blocks, Menon & Chappell, 1978. For IBM's use of the D-algorithm and TESTDETECT see Bottorff, et. al., 1977.

Some earlier work (1960 1964) would be of interest. Here were developed methods for computing the set of *all* tests that detected a given failure and in obtaining minimal sets of tests, from such constructions, detecting any of a given set of failures. The methods were largely abandoned, because of inefficiency relative to the D-algorithm, and yet they have had extensive usage in verification (Chapter 6). The *first method* of test generation (1960) consisted in generating by the P^*-algorithm (Chapter 2) the ON- and OFF- arrays (Chapter 2) for the correct (good) and malfunctioning (bad) machine and interfacing them, ON- of good with OFF- of bad OFF- of good with ON- of bad, to form the set of all tests detecting the failure. The *second method* "prunes" the graph of the design at the point of failure, i.e. the failing line is first considered as a primary input with the portion of the graph above it removed, intersections as above are formed and then the removed branch is restored and P^* (Chapter 2) is effected, to obtain the set of *all* primary input patterns detecting this failure. It is called the *method of pruning*.

Pruning was programmed and used successfully on moderate-size problems in IBM. For larger problems it encountered data explosion, e.g. on ALUs. In character-recognition logic (for the character A) developed in IBM Endicott *circa* 1963, involving only a few hundred circuits, the minimum cover (normal form) as generated by P^* would have required in excess of ten million reels of IBM magnetic tape to record it.

The *Boolean difference* method is a means to express algebraically the set of all tests to detect a given stuck failure; it requires a normal form expression for the logic. Computationally, its *algorithmic implementation* comes down either to the first or second methods outlined above. Its algebraic expression is convenient for handling small examples. Each method, because they compute *all* tests for a given failure, encounter computational bounds, both in time and space, much sooner than the D-algorithm which seeks only *one* test (cube). Of course the D-algorithm can easily be adapted to compute the set of all tests to detect a given failure but running time would be severely exacerbated.

The D-algorithm is adapted for hardware verification in Chapter 6 and for "regular-algorithm" verification in Chapter 9. An order of magnitude speedup was achieved by this adaptation.

Problems

3.1. Compute the primitive D-cubes for a 3-input AI.

3.2. Compute the *pdc*s of a 4-input Nor.

3.3. Suppose a correct circuit is an And and under failure an Xor. Compute the primitive D-cubes of failure.

3.4. In Fig. 3.2 compute a test for f stuck at 0.

3.5. In problem 3.4 use TESTDETECT to compute all failures detected by your test.

3.6. In Fig. 3.3 compute a test for line 6 stuck at 1.

3.7. In problem 3.5 use TESTDETECT to compute all failures detected by your test.

3.8. In Fig. 3.4 find a test for line 3 stuck at 0; use TESTDETECT to compute all failures detected by your test.

Bibliography

1960. Roth, J. Paul, "Diagnosis of Automata Failures," IBM Thomas J. Watson Research Center, Yorktown Heights, NY 10598, SR-114.

1964. Galey, J. M., R. E. Norby and J. P. Roth, "Techniques for the Diagnosis of Switching Circuit Failures," *IEEE Transactions on Communications and Electronics*, vol. 83, pp. 509-514.

1966. Roth, J. P., "Diagnosis of Automata Failures: A Calculus and a Method", *IBM Journal of Research & Development*, vol. 10, July, pp. 278-291.

1967. Schneider, P. R., "On the Necessity to Examine *D*-chains in Diagnostic Test Generation - An Example," *IBM Journal of Research & Development*, vol. 11, p. 114.

1967. Roth, J. Paul, Willard G. Bouricius, and Peter R. Schneider, "Programmed Algorithms to Compute Tests to Detect and Distinguish Between Failures in Logic Circuits", *IEEE Transactions on Electronic Computers*, vol. EC-16, pp. 567-580.

1967. Roth, J. P., W. G. Bouricius, W. C. Carter, and P. R. Schneider, "Phase II of an Architectural Study for a Self-Repairing Computer", U. S. Air Force, Space and Missile Systems Organization, Air Force Systems Command, Los Angeles, CA, SAMSO TR-67-106.

1969. Bouricius, W. G., W. C. Carter, K. A. Duke, J. P. Roth, P. R. Schneider, "Interactive Design of Self-Testing Circuitry", *Proceedings Purdue University*, Lafayette, Indiana, vol. I, pp. 73-80. Also IBM T. J. Watson Research Center, Yorktown Heights, NY 10598, RC 2444.

1970. Roth, J. Paul, "An Algorithm to Compute a Test to Distinguish between Two Failures in a Logic Circuit", *Proceedings IEEE Computer Society Conference*, Washington, D.C. June. Cf. also IBM T. J. Watson Research Center, Yorktown Heights, NY 10598, RC 2716.

1970. Chang, Herbert Y., Eric Manning and Gernot Metze, "Fault Diagnosis of Digital Systems", *Wiley-Interscience*, N.Y.

1970. Armstrong, D. B. Personal communication.

1972. Armstrong, D. B., "A Deductive Method of Simulating Faults in Logic Circuits," *IEEE Transactions on Electronic Computers* vol. C-21, pp. 464-471.

1974. Roth, J. Paul, "Dynamic-Failure Diagnosis", IBM T. J. Watson Research Center, Yorktown Heights, N. Y. 10598, RC 5003.

1974. Brown, Albert, "Toward a Theory of Algebraic Test Generation," IBM Corporation, Poughkeepsie, N.Y., TR 1974.

1975. Roth, J. P., "Computing Minimal Test Assemblages", *IBM Technical Disclosure Bulletin*, vol. 18, pp. 588-591.

1976. Breuer, Melvin A., Arthur D. Friedman, "Diagnosis & Reliable Design of Digital Systems," *Computer Science Press, Inc.*, Potomac, MD.

1977. Bottorff, P. S., R. E. France, N. H. Garges and E. J. Orosz, "Test Generation for Large Logic Networks," *Proceedings 14th Annual Design Automation Conference*, under sponsorship of ACM and IEEE, IEEE Catalog Number 77 CH1216-IC, New Orleans, pp. 479-485.

1978. Roth, J. P., "Improved Test-Generating *D*-algorithm," *IBM Technical Disclosure Bulletin*, vol. 20, pp. 392-394.

1978. Menon, P. R. and S. G. Chappell, "Deductive Fault Simulation with Functional Blocks," *IEEE Transactions on Electronic Computers*, vol. C-27, pp. 689-695.

1979. Brown, Albert. Personal communication.

Chapter 4

LOGIC AUTOMATION

Introduction. Most logic designs contain memory, usually signified by the existence of feedback. In this chapter, extending from Chapter 3, we consider the behavior and design of these cyclic systems. First indeterminacy is exhibited in a simple circuit. Then a simulation is described to detect indeterminacy in input sequences. A method of regular design is described in Section 4.4 which can be used expeditiously to realize any function - IBM System/360 Model 40 and IBM System/360 Model 195 were regular designs - and to eliminate races. A stronger form of regular design, known as LSSD is also scrutinized: LSSD is designed essentially for test purposes and is quite successful (Section 4.5). One problem arising in regular design, as well as in LSSD, is that of determination of total delay of acyclic portions - between registers - of logic. Section 4.6 gives a recursive and efficient method.

The language for the specification of algorithms, R-notation, employed in Chapter 1 to define MIN370 for array-logic optimization, is introduced formally in Section 4.4. In Section 4.7 the Babylonian square-root algorithm is defined in R-notation and a method, the R-compiler (1973), is used to transform this into a regular logic design precisely realizing the algorithm. The objective, to transform automatically a design algorithm written in a high-level notation into a hardware realization, is achieved in Sections 4.8 and 4.9. A hardware

87

language PL/R was introduced originally (1974) as a subset of PL/I; it is syntactically equivalent to R-notation for hardware purposes. The compiler (1974) RTRAN makes the transformation automatically and efficiently. It has been used thus far much more in conjunction with verification purposes (Chapter 6) than for the actual production of hardware.

An interesting development was the compiler R*, a kind of inverse to RTRAN, actually a decompiler of sorts. Suppose that it is desired to maintain an isomorphism between the high- and low-definitions of a logical design, e.g. between PL/R and regular logic design RLD, through engineering changes ECs, which are ordinarily made at the low detailed level. R* accepts RLDs and transforms them into PL/R or a flowchart-oriented language, which is equivalent to the original RLD, as determined by RTRAN (Section 4.9 below) and VERIFY (Chapter 6).

In Section 4.11 three extant systems for computer design, based on procedures described here, are described. One is for PLAs.

4.1. Indeterminacy in Logic. Consider in Fig. 4.1 two 2-input AI blocks connected cyclically as shown.

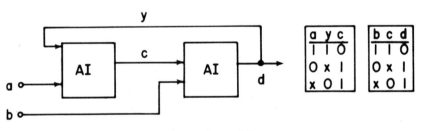

Fig. 4.1. Register with races

This design has a memory function. When $a=b=1$, both c and d are inverted upon passing through their successor AI-blocks, so that the value of the output d remains fixed. The device *remembers*, retains, the value of d. On the other hand, $d=1$ may be obtained by first imposing the input pattern 1,0 on a,b and then holding this pattern with $a=b=1$. The input pattern 0,1 on a,b gives $d=0$. Thus either output can be achieved and maintained in this primitive memory device by applying the setting patterns 1,0 or 0,1 followed by the holding pattern 1,1.

But the sequence 0,0 followed by 1,1 induces indeterminate behavior. For 0,0 will first change to either 1,0 or 0,1. Thus when 1,1 is finally imposed, the value of the output d can be either 1 or 0.

Indeterminate behavior should be avoided. If this register were part of a larger design, the larger operation would have to be organized so that this sequence never occurred.

We see from this very simple example that a logic design is not necessarily a sequential machine which requires determinacy.

Exercise.   Perform a similar analysis for a register composed of two Nors (Or followed by a Not) cyclically connected.

4.2. Function of Cyclic Designs.   For our purposes a logic design L will be defined as an arbitrary interconnection of primitives-without-memory; also specified are the primary inputs PIs and the primary outputs POs. The behavior or functioning of L is defined by its primitives through singular covers and their manner of interconnection. The restriction to acyclic logic is dropped. We do not use state tables or state diagrams: the number of states grows exponentially with the size of the design, as contrasted with the size of their singular covers which grow linearly.

Just as for the acyclic case, the function of an arbitrary interconnection L is not expressed in terms of PI/PO sequences (behavioral description). The combinatorics prevent this definition for sizeable networks. It is expressed by means of its cover, which defines the function of each block in terms of the variables of the blocks that feed it.

A first problem that one must solve for any arbitrary L is whether or not any given sequence has indeterminacies. Eichelberger (1965) provided such means, under certain assumptions.

Even acyclic designs may have indeterminacies if we consider sequences of primary-input patterns. For example, the Exclusive-or design of Fig. 4.2 may have a spurious output 0 between two correct outputs 1,1 corresponding to the input sequence 1,0 followed by 0,1 (for both inputs may or may not switch simultaneously).

To ascertain the existence of indeterminacies we reintroduce the symbol x here to stand for the indeterminate case: x may be equal to either 1 or 0. Pursuing first our design in Fig. 4.2 we would insert into the PI-sequence 1,0; 0,1 the indeterminate x for each change of input, here two:

$$1,0; \; x,x; \; 0,1;$$

We see immediately that the indeterminate inputs x,x yield an indeterminate output x.

Exercise. Examine all sequences of length 2 of Fig. 4.2. for indeterminate behavior.

4.3. Simulation of Cyclic Logic. Let us first take the register of Fig. 4.1. Consider on *a,b* the sequence 0,1 followed by 1,1. To ascertain the possible indeterminacy of this PI-sequence, we insert the cube x,1 to obtain 0,1; x,1; 1,1. Now 0,1 yields the output on *d*, of 0, with a 1 on *c*. Shifting to the not-completely-known PI-pattern x,1, we see that *d* has input values x,0 but the 0 dominates for, as shown from its cover, whatever value x has, *d* has value 1. The final pattern 1,1 locks the value of *d* to 1. No indeterminacy.

Exercise. Simulate Fig. 4.1 in similar fashion with patterns 1,0; 1,1. Also 0,0; 1,1.

The 3-valued simulation of cyclic designs depends in general upon the order of sequencing the logic elements (or upon an unwarranted

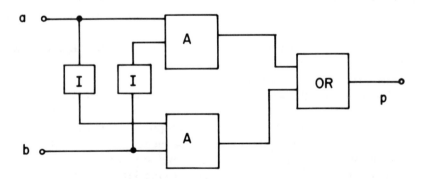

Fig. 4.2. Indeterminate acyclic design

assumption of state-variable signals) in the simulation.   In a study (1971) in test generation (cf. Section 5.1) by Putzolu and the author this was done by adroitly cutting feedback loops to introduce state variables, making an iterative design of p copies (Fig. 5.3) for input patterns of length p, setting pseudo-inputs to x and applying alternating sequences of input patterns and indeterminate patterns, with x inserted between changing patterns.   This method has the disadvantage that the results depend upon the method of cutting.

Simulators have been constructed for 5-valued logics, using u for rising and d for falling, to represent further conditions in addition to 0,1 and x (1979 vanCleemput).   See also 1976, Breuer and Friedman, for 8- and 9-valued simulations.

We turn now to a method of design which eliminates the indeterminacies in the design but yet makes it possible to realize any sequential function.

4.4.   Regular Logic Design.   The difficulty with arbitrarily constructed designs is that there are input sequences which have indeterminate output sequences, as we have seen from the first part of this chapter. The same problem arises in attempting test generation for such designs. Putzolu and I (1971) (cf. Chapter 5) treated a logic design as a randomly connected network of logic primitives, with PIs and POs specified; elaborate procedures were developed to select the feedback networks for cutting; an iterative design was defined based upon this cut design; tests for failures in this iterative model were computed; then we *simulated* the test sequence only to find out, for sizeable networks, that they frequently contained indeterminacies.   We now define a general method of design which is guaranteed to have no indeterminacies.

A *regular logic module* RLM consists of acyclic logic or if feedback is desired between an input/output pair, then a pair of registers is inserted in the loop, each gated at different clock times.   A *regular logic design* RLD is an interconnection of RLMs.   Frequently we shall term an RLD simply a *regular design* or *R-design*.

Proof that regular logic designs are well defined.   We assume it is evident that an RLM without feedback is well defined; for instance, it can be transformed by P^* (Section 2.7) into a 2-level realization, specifically, into a PLA.

Consider next an RLM with exactly one feedback loop, being realized by a line having inserted within it two registers gated by clocks, *clock* 1 and *clock* 2, having non-overlapping "rise" times: this implies that the two clock inputs to the registers never are 1 at the same time. When *clock* 1 is *on* (i.e. 1) then the primary input values on the PI and the pseudo-inputs S1, released from the register by the *clock* 1 signal, are gated into the logic. The subsequent signals in the internal logic filter to the primary outputs PO and to the "pseudo primary outputs" SO, therefore "latched" until *clock* 2 comes on. The delay (cf. Section 3.9) between *clock* 1 and *clock* 2 is assumed to be sufficiently large so that the PO and SO values are stabilized before new values are gated by *clock* 2 to the input registers. Thus, as determined by the clock signals, *clock* 1 and *clock* 2, the POs and SOs respond at "*clock* 2 time" to the signals on the PIs and SIs at clock 1.

Exercise. Use mathematical induction to define an RLM with k feedback loops; prove that it defines a function.

Exercise. Suppose we have r RLMs whose interconnection is well defined as an RLD, and we wish to add another RLM to the interconnection. Assuming independent clocks for each RLM, sketch the result of thus joining $r+1$ of them and prove, using mathematical induction, that the resultant RLD defines well a new function.

   R-design has been used before: on the IBM System 360/40, justifying economy, and on the IBM System 360/195, justifying speed. We do not in general require the shift-registers in order to render testing acyclic, as is done by M. Williams and Angell (1973) and Eichelberger and T. Williams, (1977) (cf. Section 4.5). We now have a logical format in which failure-diagnosis, test-generation, and verification can take place without fear that races, hazards, oscillations, generally indeterminacies, can interfere. Furthermore R-design supplies a target for compilation from a high-level language (cf. Sections 4.7, 4.8).

4.5. LSSD. As we shall see in the next two chapters, even with a regular logic design, it is difficult, combinatorially speaking, to generate tests for failures and to verify the correctness of designs. Both for testing and verification, it is expedient to consider an iterative model of the design, in general with several copies interconnected - we found at least three were usually necessary - of the original design, and this considerably exacerbated the computations.

   A method of design was devised, initially by Williams and Angell and finally by Eichelberger, which reduced these cyclic design problems to acyclic analysis problems. We shall discuss *level sensitive scan design* LSSD of Eichelberger. It is convenient first to explain the

SCAN approach (1964) as used on IBM System/360. Here special registers and I/O pins were employed so that, at time of test, the design was logically rendered acyclic. This method could not be moved bodily into LSI or VLSI technology for chip testing because of its need for a substantial number of extra pins, which are simply unavailable on chips. Williams and Angell (1973) supplied additional logic to the SCAN latches in such manner that their contents, at time of testing, could be connected in the form of a shift-register (one or more) so that their contents could be read in (SCANIN) or read out (SCANOUT) through the services of only a few pins. Eichelberger developed a production augmentation called LSSD and this system is widely used.

4.6. Delay Calculation. With each primitive circuit is associated a positive number called its *delay*, which is the amount of time it takes the circuit to respond fully to a change of input pattern. In general it is a function of its fan-in and fan-out. In R-design there is no constraint on the delays of individual circuits but there is the necessity that the sum of the delays between two paired registers not exceed the total prescribed clock delay between the registers. We present here an algorithm for the total delay of an acyclic logic design (1973 Roth). Furthermore we use SEGMENT (Chapter 2) to split the problem into several problems, each with one primary output.

DELAY. We assume an *intrinsic delay* with each block, that being the time required for it to respond completely to a change of input signals. Given a path in the design, its *path delay* is the sum of the intrinsic delays of the blocks in the path. The *terminal delay* of a block is the maximum delay of the paths linking it to the primary output d. The *total block delay tbd* to d is the sum of the intrinsic and terminal delays. The computation goes by induction. The block at level 1 is the primary output; its *tbd* is its intrinsic delay. Having computed the *tbd*s for all blocks of level n-1, the terminal delay of a block at level n is the maximum of the *tbd*s of the blocks it feeds. Its *tbd* is the sum of the terminal delay and its intrinsic delay. The *delay* of the total design is then the maximum tbd of all (primary input) blocks.

4.7 Regular Notation or R-notation was defined in Section 1.5. It developed as a method of description of certain mathematical algorithms. It grew out of the singular cubical notation of Chapter 1. Implicit in its development is the ability to transform such

"R-algorithms" into a logical realization, a logical design, that will perform the R-algorithm in "hardware", i.e. logic.

First we consider a particular example, then a general program.

Transform of R-algorithm into R-design. As an indication of generality of this process let us consider the Newton-Raphson algorithm for finding the square root of a number. Because the Babylonians had it earlier, we denote it B. The number whose root we wish is n; r is an approximate root; e the desired degree ~of approximation; y is the calculated root. Thus the "head expression" for the algorithm is written $y=B(n,r,e)$. The first step in the algorithm is to compute a new approximate root $s=(n+r*r)/2*r$; in the algorithmic rendition this will be denoted $s=S(n,r)$. The next step is to evaluate the "goodness" of this new approximation, as determined by a binary variable $a=|n-s*s|<e$; when $(n-s*s)$ in absolute value is less than e then $a=1$; otherwise, 0. Thus a is the signal, the variable, which terminates the algorithm. The evaluation of a is written for convenience $a=A(n,s,e)$. When $a=1$ then a satisfactory solution has been obtained; this condition is expressed $a=1\Rightarrow y=s$; on the other hand if $a=0$ a new approximation is to be made. This is expressed recursively as $a=1\Rightarrow y=B(n,s,e)$; where the new approximation s has been substituted for the original r. Then the entire Babylonian algorithm would be written

$$<y=B(n,r,e)=:s=S(n,r);\ a=A(n,s,e);\ (a=1)\Rightarrow y=s;\ (a=0)\Rightarrow y=B(n,s,e)>$$

Now we demonstrate via Fig. 4.3 how this arithmetic algorithm can be transformed into a regular logic design, defined in Section 4.4. First we represent the "macros" $s=S(n,r)$; and $a=A(n,s,e)$; by boxes, whose interiors would be defined by further code. Next is the decision, depending upon the value of a, as to what action to take next. This is expressed by the two formulas: $(a=1)\Rightarrow y=s$; $(a=0)\Rightarrow y=B(n,s,e)$; rendered by one decision box, truth table, with a and y as columns, as shown. This has entries: if $a=1$ then $y=s$; if $a=0$ then $y=x$, i.e. it is as yet indeterminate. It is easily rendered into detailed logic (1974, Roth and Levy). The variables s and a which are used in the next iteration of the computation, are fed into a register. In turn s and a are fed back to a second register, gated in non-overlapping manner from the first register. There they feed another decision table only implicit in the R-notational description. It has to be decided whether the original argument r or the new approximation s is to be fed back into the "Babylonian machine". If s is not sufficient-

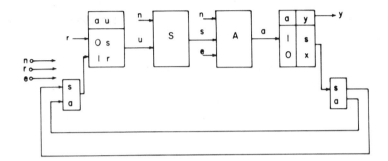

Fig. 4.3. Babylonian square-root machine

ly good according to the "A criterion", then $a=0$ and the new approximation s will be used in another computation. Hence the entry

$$a \ u$$
$$0 \ s$$

where u denotes the input to S.   On the other hand if $a=1$, the approximation is satisfactory, the solution is $y=s$ and the Babylonian machine is ready for new data, in particular a new r. Thus the entry

$$a \ u$$
$$1 \ r \ .$$

There is no difficulty in reducing each of the boxes and registers to a specific logic design, an LSI implementation, hence an overall R-design for the algorithm.

The "R-compiler" (1974 Roth and Levy) transforms R-algorithms, algorithms written in R-notation, into hardware realizations. This compiler has had scant usage. For a specifically hardware language PL/R, a small subset of PL/I, Harry Halliwell wrote a compiler RTRAN which transforms hardware-design algorithms into R-designs (Section 4.8). RTRAN has had extensive usage for verification purposes (Chapter 6).

Exercise. Regular design having been defined above in Section 4.4, outline the definition of transforming an R-algorithm *in general* into a regular hardware-design realization. In Chapter 9 this is done for an *iterative* regular logic design (with a bound, specified by the designer), as a realization of an R-algorithm.

4.8. PL/R. As indicated by a hardware rendition of the Babylonian algorithm, it appears direct to transform an R-algorithm into an R-design. The R-notation is a general algorithmic language. It was used to describe: the 2-level multiple-output minimization algorithm (Chapter 1); the D-algorithm for computing tests for failures (Chapter 3); and a sizeable number of arithmetic algorithms. It appeared time-consuming to develop *ab initio* a compiler which would transform R-algorithms into efficient R-designs.

Instead Harry Halliwell (1974, Halliwell & Roth) defined a minuscule subset PL/R of PL/I, tailored for logical algorithms. Then the PL/I compilers were utilized substantially in the task of developing the hardware compiler, which was called RTRAN.

Presently PL/R is no longer a subset of PL/I but a language in its own right (translated by RTRAN into PL/I), and we shall describe its current syntax. Its primitives contain the A &; Or $|$; Xor $\neg =$; Not $\neg$; if-then-else; and DOs.

A PL/R program starts, in the first line, with an = sign, followed by the name of the function, followed by names of the primary inputs and outputs, these enclosed in parentheses, and ended by a semicolon. For instance the 3-input majority function MAJ3, whose implementation was given in Fig. 2.4, has as its first line

$$=MAJ3(a,b,c,m);$$

specifying its primary input and output variables. The next line specifies the primary input variables together with their dimensions. Variables are binary or vectors of binary digits. For MAJ3 the input variables a,b,c would be written

Inputs a,b,c;

The fact that they are binary variables (of dimension 1) is specified by
default. An input variable v of r bits would be expressed as $v(r)$.
Next the outputs would be similarly specified; for MAJ3,

Outputs m;

Next the remaining internal variables, together with their dimensions are listed in a DCL statement: for MAJ3 there are none. Finally the feedback variables, into whose lines are placed the pairs of
registers, are specified by a declaration of the form

REGISTER ALPHA(A),...,BETA(B);

where ALPHA,...,BETA are the register names and A,...,B are their
respective dimensions. (The default starting position for a dimensional
variable in PL/R is 0, rather than 1 as in PL/I.) What follows is the
logic of the algorithm.

   For example, the function MAJ3 is expressed in PL/R completely
as

$=$MAJ3(a,b,c,m);
inputs a,b,c;
outputs m;
$m=a\&b \mid b\&c \mid c\&a$;

It is unnecessary to have an END; statement as in PL/I.
   It is possible to specify function in PL/R by means of DO statements, as shown by the one-byte Arithmetic and Logic Unit ALU8
given below; for simplicity this produces only the functions And, Or,
Xor, Plus.

```
1     =ALU8(R,S,T,A,O,X,P,KI,KO);
2     INPUT R(8),S(8),A,O,X,P,KI;
3     OUTPUT T(8),KO;
4     DCL TA(8),TO(8),TX(8),TP(8),K(8);
5     TA=R&S;
6     TO=R | S;
7     TX=¬R&S | ¬S&R;
8     K(0)=KI;
9     DO J=0 to 6;
10    K(J+1)=K(J)&TO(J) | ¬K(J)&TA(J);
11    END;
12    TP=¬TX&K | ¬K&TX;
13    T=TA&A | TO&O | TX&X | TP&P;
14    KO=K(7)&TO(7) | ¬K(7)&TA(7);
```

In PL/R it is possible to employ *macros,* subroutines used in a program; these macros are defined elsewhere. The use of macros is illustrated by the bad parity function PT2BAD on 4 (=2**2) bits which uses as a macro the parity PT1 on 2 bits. The arrow in statement 4 defines A0 to be the first two bits of A; similarly 5 defines A1 to be the last.

```
1     =PT2BAD(A,P);
2     INPUT A(4);
3     OUTPUT P;
4     DCL A0(2) -> A( +0);
5     DCL A1(2) -> A( +2);
6     DCL B(2);
7     BAD=PT1(A0);
8     B(0)=¬BAD;
9     B(1)=PT1(A1);
10    P=PT1(B);
```

The IF THEN ELSE instruction is prescribed in a Boolean manner in order to be close to the resulting implementation. Thus the statement *if a then y=f; else y=g* is rendered $y=a\&f | \neg a\&g$.

4.9. RTRAN is a compiler which transforms a PL/R program into a regular logic design RLD. It first transforms the PL/R into PL/I. Then the PL/I optimizing compiler transforms this PL/I image into *raw logic,* using solely 2-input Ands and Ors, with negations allowed on variables. E.g., the raw-logic implementation of the majority function MAJ3 becomes

R-FILE FOR MAJ3

```
A
1    2 = PI
B
1    3 = PI
C
1    4 = PI
1    5 = AND 3    2
1    6 = AND 4    3
1    7 = AND 2    4
1    8 = OR   6    5
1    9 = OR   7    8
M
1   10 = PO  9
```

Here the primary inputs A,B,C are encoded as the numbers 2,3,4. Then the logic follows; e.g. 5 = AND 3 2 means 5 = AND(3,2), etc. Finally the primary output M is identified with the line 10.

Following is the raw-logic implementation of PT2BAD, the PL/R function given above. In the PL/R program A was declared to be a 4-bit primary-input variable and these are encoded in the number names 2,3,4,5. Note that in line 6, line 2 is negated.

$$6 = \text{AND} \quad 3 \ -2$$

R-FILE FOR PT2BAD

```
A
1    2  = PI
1    3  = PI
1    4  = PI
1    5  = PI
1    6  = AND        3      - 2
1    7  = AND        2      - 3
1    8  = OR         7       6
1    9  = AND        5      - 4
1   10  = AND        4      - 5
1   11  = OR        10       9
1   12  = AND       11       8
1   13  = AND       - 8     -11
1   14  = OR        13      12
P
```

1   15 = PO   14

Following this is the "hardware" implementation in AI (and N) technology. This is a 1-input, 2-input logic technology, used primarily for simplicity for subsequent verification procedures.

R-FILE FOR PT2BAD

A

1	2	= PI		
1	3	= PI		
1	4	= PI		
1	5	= PI		
1	6	= N	2	
1	7	= AI	3	6
1	8	= N	3	
1	9	= AI	2	8
1	10	= AI	9	7
1	11	= N	4	
1	12	= AI	5	11
1	13	= N	5	
1	14	= AI	4	13
1	15	= AI	14	12
1	16	= AI	15	10
1	17	= N	10	
1	18	= N	15	
1	19	= AI	17	18
1	20	= AI	19	16

P

1	21	= PO	20	

The raw-logic implementation of ALU8 has 168 blocks. The 2-input AI (and N) implementation has 200.

Exercise. Define PT3, parity on 8 bits using PT2...PT8, parity on 256 bits, using PT4. (PT8 yields around 1000 circuits.)

4.10. R*, Inverse to RTRAN. We have seen, with PL/R and RTRAN, a system for converting a high-level specification of a hardware algorithm into a detailed regular logic design. Under certain circumstances it is desirable to perform the inverse transformation, to take a detailed regular logic design, an RLD, and produce a PL/R algorithm that is equivalent to it. It would be equivalent in the sense that, if this PL/R algorithm were in turn converted into hardware by RTRAN, or were converted manually correctly, then this design would be equivalent to the original hardware design, as determined by VERIFY (Chapter 6). In this section we describe an algorithm for this inverse transformation (1975). It has been embodied into a PL/I program RSTAR or R* by Bryan A. Lewis of IBM in England. Applying R* to an RLD yields a description, largely Boolean, which is independent of the eccentricities of its technology. It is therefore in a form enabling it to be reduced, by RTRAN, to any new technology.

Furthermore if the original design had a high-level (PL/R) description, it would be obsoleted by *manual* changes in the RLD. With R*, these engineering changes ECs could be automatically updated in the PL/R, to keep the high- and low-levels of the design in agreement.

Given a regular logic design, we assume that the registers, in pairs, are declared. One register of each pair is appropriately treated as if it were a primary input; its companion is treated as an output. In the (optimizing) procedures that are applied in R*, the registers, and their corresponding pseudo-inputs and pseudo-outputs retain their identity: there is no attempt made at state reduction.

With this identification of registers as PIs and POs in the RLD, the problem of recovering a high-level (PL/R) specification from a detailed logic design is reduced to the acyclic case.

The first step in R* is the *P**-algorithm as described in Chapter 2. This takes each output and successively eliminates logic blocks, reducing the original multi-level design into one of two levels. Thus the function of each output and pseudo-output is reduced to a 2-level cover or And-Or realization.

The second step which may be interleaved with the first, is to reduce the size of these multiple-output (actually several single-output) covers; this is done by using the approximate reduction technique SHRINK, described in Chapter 1. SHRINK will automatically combine cubes from several outputs.

Step 3 is a controlled factorization (Section 2.8) of the 2-level realization produced by SHRINK. It is controlled in the sense that the user is able to specify a limit on the number of levels of logic that his timing requirements will allow. As a tool then, the designer could opt in favor of speed with few levels, or economy with many levels.

The final step is the translation of the multiple-level design, as produced by step 3, into the high-level design language. In our case this would be PL/R although we have found it equally simple for another language.

In the programming implementation of RTRAN, *R*-design is in the form of LSSD. From the point of view of test-generation and verification this indeed is the simplest form of implementation. It requires, however, additional hardware.

4.11. Systems for Computer Design. In this exposé, elements for systems of computer design have been given. In this chapter languages PL/R and RLD, for high- and low-level hardware descriptions, have been presented. Algorithms RTRAN and R* have been described to transform, usually in an efficient manner, from high- to low- design levels and vice versa. Different forms of design, R-design and LSSD, have also been defined and the compilers RTRAN and R* have used these. A regular method of design have been given to guarantee determinacy and for computation of delays in acyclic portions of logic - in particular of R-designs or LSSD-designs.

Chapters 3 and 5 present methods for the generation of tests to detect failures in logic. Chapter 6 contains algorithms for verification to assure correctness of designs, a step essential to large scale integration LSI. Chapter 1 has algorithms for the design of two-level logic used as an essential part of programming-logic-array PLA designs.

If these programs are put together into a system, one has an effective tool for the design of computers. Using these as building blocks we shall describe three systems for the design of logic, two for random logic, and one for PLAs.

System for Computer Design SCD is an ensemble of programs for the design of logic (1974). The design is specified at a high level, in PL/R or a hardware flowchart language. The compiler RTRAN transforms a PL/R-algorithm into an R-design, conforming to the requirements of some technology, with regard to fan-in, fan-out, powering, etc. For control logic the technology-based RTRAN produces correctly, and in a short time, logic as efficient as manually produced logic. For arithmetic logic, designers were able to do better.

As described above R* is a kind of inverse to RTRAN, accepting an RLD and transforming it into PL/R or other high-level hardware language. Engineering changes ECs are made in general to the RLD level, and with R* it becomes automatic to keep the PL/R and RLD updated together.

Furthermore R* can be a tool for redesign activities (1978). Suppose a hardware design A is in the form of an RLD in some technology and it is desired to "remap" (redesign) the design in another technology. With R*, A is converted to, lifted up to, a high-level PL/R (or other) algorithmic specification. Then, utilizing RTRAN adjusted to the new technology, a new implementation in the technology is generated, all with complete automaticity.

The algorithm VERIFY described in Chapter 6 has the ability to accept two RLDs, with a one-to-one correspondence between PIs, POs and registers, and to ascertain completely whether or not they are functionally equivalent. Thus VERIFY can compare two detailed low-level RLDs. Suppose one has a PL/R-algorithm R and an RLD T and wishes to compare their function. First one forms the RLD-realization S of R under RTRAN. Then VERIFY determines the equivalence between S and T and hence between R and T. Likewise one can compare completely two R-algorithms X and Y as:

$$\text{VERIFY (RTRAN}(X), \text{RTRAN}(Y)).$$

Logic Automation Complex. A predecessor to SCD is the Logic Automation Complex (1965, Roth). The input, the high-level definition, is a *sequence chart*, a kind of sequenced flow-chart and was used to define complex control operations. An analyzer translates a sequence chart first into raw logic consisting of Ands and Ors allowing for negated inputs and outputs. Then an implementation program CIMPL converts this into the IBM System/360 technology SLT, obeying the logical constraints of SLT: fan-in, fan-out, powering, logic types. Only local optimization is performed, none of the global simplifications as in R^* in SCD.

CIMPL could also be used, with a preprocessor, to simplify and implement logic defined in Boolean equations. This was used by K. A. Duke in Hursley, England, with the author, to translate Boolean specifications of the Arithmetic and Logic Unit into the complete SLT design for the IBM System/360 Model 40. This design was also used in the Model 30. The logic automation complex contains programs for factorization, automatic logic drawing, and predecessors to MIN370 and R^*.

PLA System. A third system for automatic design of logic was also formed wherein the "target" design was PLAs. Essentially, in this system the logic is specified initially in a high-level language such as PL/R. This high-level algorithm is thoroughly simulated. Then RTRAN together with P^* is employed to transform this hardware design into a cover in two levels (Chapter 1) corresponding to an initial PLA implementation. Then SHRINK or, for small problems EXACT, is used to effect a simplification in this PLA reduction.

This automatic approach was compared with manual designs, essentially by performing R* on already completed manual designs - there were no extant flowcharts going with the manual designs - to obtain a PL/R definition of the designs and then by applying the SHRINK(P*(RTRAN)) treatment to them. For the designs compared, the manual and automatic were of about the same cost and complexity.

One could also verify correctness of a PLA design by comparing it with a high-level description using RTRAN and VERIFY.

Designing With Macros. In RTRAN, as described above, macros are allowed in the definition of PL/R functions but the macro structure is destroyed in the implementation. RTRAN behaves like the PL/I compilers; it destroys the macro structure. In several of the subsequent operations, embedding (Chapter 7), testing (Chapter 5), verification (Chapter 6) and redesigning, R* is useful to preserve these structures. A method of macro preservation described here is simple and effective.

Macro Notation. In PL/R a function, here called macro, is specified by a sequence of PL/R or macro statements. In their implementation all the logic, whether from a PL/R statement or macro, is expressed as an undifferentiated list. The method of preserving the macros is to implement via RTRAN each macro individually and to prefix the label of each circuit therein with the name of the macro. Each macro is so implemented only once: repetitions of a given macro are indicated by inserting a number following the macro-name prefix.

If macro A is a portion of macro B then the circuits produced by RTRAN will have as prefixes the names of both of the macros to which it belongs, in descending order. A given macro would be implemented only once in this schema.

Now let us consider test-generation. From Chapters 3 and 5, runtime is an exponential function of size of the logic. But it is possible to take advantage of knowledge of its macro structure. In particular, it may be possible to test an entire macro *in situ*. This provides a solution to the test-point-insertion problem (1971, Dauber).

Essentially we must obtain control over the primary inputs of the macro as well as to be able to read its primary outputs. For this purpose we introduce the universal function schema from Chapter 8 to obtain control over the inputs and, for the outputs, we use the shift-register approach of Chapter 5.

To obtain input control we introduce a new input whose value is held by an element of a shift-register. Both the old macro PI and the new PI enter AI blocks whose other entries are elements of a shift-register.   Under normal operation the old PI will be the input; under test, the new PI.

For the outputs, a PO will fan into elements of a shift-register, which will be gated out at test time.

4.12.   Other Work. Other logic design languages have been defined - notably the digital design language of Dietmeyer and Duley (1975). They have a translator for this language to Boolean equations.   According to Dietmeyer (1978) this system has been used by a Japanese computer manufacturer, for simulation purposes.

Five-valued simulators for more precise information concerning indeterminacies have been described (1979 vanCleemput).

Cornish (1976) of Texas Instruments discusses an interesting use of regular design in maintenance and testing of a large, fast machine.

Problems

4.1.   Outline briefly the structure of a compiler which preserves macro structures as in Section 4.11.

4.2.   Suppose that a *board* consists of an interconnection of a number of *chips*, consisting of LSSD logic.   Suppose that you already have tests for failures for the individual chips.   Devise a design of the board so that these tests can be utilized to test the chips mounted on board.

Bibliography

1960.   Roth, J. Paul, "Minimization over Boolean Trees", *IBM Journal of Research & Development*, vol. 4, pp. 543-558.

1964.   Carter, W. C., H. C. Montgomery, R. J. Preiss, and H. J. Reinheimer, "Design of Serviceability Features for the IBM System/360", *IBM Journal of Research & Development*, vol. 8, pp. 115-126.

1965.   Eichelberger, E. B., "Hazard Detection in Combinational and Sequential Circuits", *IBM Journal of Research & Development*, vol. 9, pp. 90-99.

1965.   Roth, J. P., "Systematic Design of Automata", *American Federation of Information Processing Societies AFIPS*, Proceedings of Fall Joint Computer Conference, vol. 27, pp. 1093-1100.

1969.   Duley, J. R. and D. L. Dietmeyer, "Translation of a DDL Digital System Specification to Boolean Equations", *IEEE Transactions on Computers*, vol. C-18, pp. 305-318.

1971.   Dauber, P. S. Personal communication.

1971.   Putzolu, Gianfranco R. and J. Paul Roth, "A Heuristic Algorithm for the Testing of Asynchronous Circuits", *IEEE Transactions on Computers*, vol. C-20, pp. 639-647.

1973.   Roth, J. Paul, "Algorithm for Delay Determination", *IBM Technical Disclosure Bulletin*, vol. 15, January, pp. 144,5.

1973.   Williams, M. J. Y., and J. B. Angell, "Enhancing Testability of Large Scale Integrated Circuits via Test Points and Additional Logic", *IEEE Transactions on Computers*, vol. C22, pp. 46-60.

1974.   Roth, J. Paul and Leon S. Levy, "*R*-notation and its Usage in Computer Design", *Proceedings of 2nd Jerusalem Symposium on Information Technology*, pp. 589-603.

1974. Halliwell, H. and J. P. Roth, "System for Computer Design", *IBM Technical Disclosure Bulletin*, vol. 17, October, pp. 1517-1519.

1975. Roth, J. P., "Generating a High-Level Algorithmic Definition of a Detailed Logic Design", *IBM Technical Disclosure Bulletin*, vol. 18, pp. 1267f.

1975. Dietmeyer, Donald L. and James R. Duley, "Register Transfer Languages and their Translation", appearing in "Digital System Design Automation: Languages, Simulation and Data Base", edited by M. A. Breuer, *Computer Science Press, Inc.*, Potomac, MD., pp. 117-218.

1976. Cornish, M., "The *D*-algorithm for Sequential Circuits: An Extension and its Application", *IEEE Computer Society Repository*.

1976. Breuer, Melvin A. and Arthur D. Friedman, "Diagnosis & Reliable Design of Digital Systems", *Computer Science Press, Inc.*, Potomac, MD, pp. 190-201.

1977. Eichelberger, E. B., and T. W. Williams, "A Logic Design Structure for LSI Testability", *Proceedings of the fourteenth annual Design Automation Conference under joint sponsorship of the ACM and IEEE*, New Orleans, IEEE Catalog No. 77 CH1216-11.

1978. Roth, J. P., "Macro Physical Design", *IBM Invention Disclosure Bulletin*, vol. 20, pp. 3792-3794.

1978. Roth, J. Paul, "Automatic Remap", *IBM Technical Disclosure Bulletin*, vol. 20, pp. 5443-4.

1979. vanCleemput, William M. Personal communication.

Chapter 5

SEQUENTIAL TESTING

Introduction. In Chapter 3 we introduced methods for the generation of tests for failures in arbitrary *acyclic* logic designs. The D-algorithm for computing a test for a failure and its converse TESTDETECT together form a basis for obtaining an ensemble of tests detecting any of a specified list of failures of an acyclic logic design.

Testing cyclic logic is more difficult. We shall describe three methods of design and test generation and allude to others. One of the most direct and useful methods of dealing with cyclic diagnosis is by the use of LSSD (Section 4.5), which introduces extra hardware that in effect renders the design acyclic for testing purposes.

The first method (Section 5.1 Loop-cutter) involves: cutting all feedback loops of any logic design; computing tests in an iterated construction of the resulting acyclic design; attempting to apply these potential tests to the original design. Because of possible indeterminacies of these tests in the original design the method does not always work. LSSD testing is disposed of easily in Section 5.2 since by design it reduces to acyclic testing.

Regular design (Section 4.4) was developed originally as a method of design for which testing for failures was possible. It is a natural way to design. It eliminates indeterminacies and allows a test method for regular logic, specifically an extension of the D-algorithm, with no addition of hardware (Section 5.3). TESTDETECT, our candidate to supplant fault (= failure) simulation, is extended in Section 5.4 to regular (cyclic) designs.   The remaining sections treat delay testing and short testing, with the final section discussing other work.

5.1.   Loop-cutter.   First we give a description of work (1971) by Putzolu and the author to consider the test process for *arbitrary* logic networks.   In this study, a logic design L is defined as an arbitrary interconnection of acyclic logic primitives, having no macro memory cells.   In general these designs contain cycles so that they have memory as part of their function.   Thus the behavior of the designs, with or without failure, could not be characterized by input- and corresponding output-patterns of length one alone.   Yet no memory cells were included in the logic design description to facilitate rendition of their sequential behavior.

The core of the method is a technique for adroitly "cutting the loops".   This was executed in an elaborate attempt at selection of the cuts so that insertion of appropriate delays at the point of cuts would not modify the behavior of the circuit.   One criterion was to seek "tight" loops, i.e., those which had few primitives in them, in the expectation that these tight loops would correspond to register elements, latches, in some higher-level specification of the design.

First all primary inputs are labelled successively with integers starting with 1.   In general a block is labelled if all of its predecessors are labelled.   Some blocks which cannot be so labelled lie on a loop.   Consider a loop, some of whose inputs are labelled.   For each block in the loop compute the "tightness factor", being the minimum number of blocks in a loop going through the block.   It was our assumption that "tightest loops" correspond to registers.   A tightest loop being uncovered, a cut at its output is made and further assignments, according to the above criteria, are in general possible.   This process is repeated if necessary.   If there are no inner loops, other criteria are used.   A block A in a loop feeding a block B not in the loop is cut at the output of A.

The loop-cutter procedure is illustrated in Fig. 5.1.   Two criteria are applied in the following order: 1.   cut at the outputs of inner loops; 2.   cut at the outputs of main loops.   In the diagram only 7 can be immediately assigned.   A loop must be cut.   Arbitrarily select block 8 as the starting point in locating the first loop.   The successors to block 8 are:

9, 10, 12, 13, 14, 11, 8

Its unassigned predecessors are:

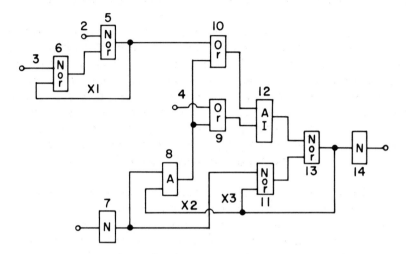

Fig. 5.1. Example of loop-cutter

13, 11, 12, 9, 10, 8, 5, 6

Since block 5 is a predecessor but not a successor, it becomes the next candidate for examination. Its successors are:

6, 5 and the successors to 8 as listed above.

Its predecessors are:

6, 5

Since this set is entirely contained in the set of successors, this set constitutes the elements of the first loop,

5, 6.

The tightness factor for both elements is 2 and therefore no inner loop can be identified. The first criterion cannot be applied and the loop must be cut where it feeds other blocks, i.e., at the output of block 5.   But, since it is only the loop that must be cut, the cut is made where block 5 feeds into block 6, X1 on the diagram.

Now blocks 6, 5 may be assigned and another loop is encountered.   This is located as before and is found to consist of blocks 8, 9, 10, 11, 12, 13.   The tightness factors are now calculated and it is found that blocks 8, 9, 10, 12 have a tightness factor of 4 and blocks 11, 13 have a tightness factor of 2.   Therefore, blocks 11, 13 are elements of one or more inner loops.   Since block 11 feeds only block 13, its output is not an immediate candidate for cutting.   Block 13, on the other hand, feeds not only block 11, but also block 8.   Block 14 is not in the main loop and is not considered here.   The main loop is therefore cut where block 13 feeds block 8, i.e., at X2.   Blocks 8, 9, 10, 12 may now be assigned, and the loop 11, 13 is encountered.   As with the first loop, there is no inner loop and the cut is made at the output of 13, i.e., at X3.   Now the remaining blocks may be assigned and all loops have been cut.

If a test of length p is sought for some failure F, then p copies of the cut design are interconnected to form an iterative and acyclic representation of the original design.   The D-algorithm (Chapter 3) is then adapted (1971), to compute a test for the failure F, having in the iterative model p manifestations.   The test $T(p)$ so computed is then a candidate for a test for the original F in the original network L.   To determine its validity it is simulated to detect indeterminacies, as described in Chapter 4.   There is no guarantee that such a test would be devoid of indeterminacies.

As the size of L increases the occurrence of indeterminacies tends to increase.   Thus it is not an effective method for test generation for large random networks.

Suppose then it is desired to find a test for a particular failure, say line 7 stuck at 1, in the original design S, Fig. 5.1.   To use this method you must decide how many copies you will use in the iterative model IM of L.   Say two copies.   You must also decide the point of origin at which to start the D-drive.   In IM this could be one of two locations.   Let us start D-drive from the second timeframe.

The generation of the test in IM has few surprises.   There is a failure in each time frame.   The pseudo-inputs must remain at x and no pseudo-output can be used.   Going through the D-algorithm extended to the iterative model we derive the test sequence speaking in terms of primary inputs: 0011; 10x0.   There is a merging process among the sequences produced by DALG (D-algorithm program), which has the intent to remove races and reduce sequence length: for this simple case the sequence is reduced to: 0011; 1010. This happens also to be a sequence of length two. For more details see 1971.

Next we discuss testing designs having LSSD which effectively reduces sequential to acyclic testing.

5.2.   LSSD Testing. A candidate for a *test* for failure F in a design L with feedback in general must consist of a sequence of primary input patterns. Such sequences will generally harbor indeterminacies. If so, these candidates must be rejected. Indeed that is the shortcoming of the loop-cutter method of section 5.1. In this and, to a lesser extent, in the next section, constraints will be imposed on L in such manner that the tests computed will be determinate and, in this section will be reduced to singleton tests: by design, sequential testing is reduced to acyclic.

There are two ideas. The first, regular design, Chapter 4 and 1970, assigns to each feedback loop in L a pair of registers gated at nonoverlapping clock times. If sufficient time is allowed for transition of the intervening acyclic network, then the design becomes determinate. But we are still left with a sequential diagnosis problem. The second answer was to insert some SCAN (1964) in the registers: this means to design the registers so that their contents may be, read-into at test-time and, read-out at another time. Effectively this reduces sequential to acyclic diagnosis.

With the advent of LSI this "Fault-Locating Technology" was no longer feasible: it required an excessive number of I/O pins on the chip. (It is roughly that the perimeter of a square increases linearly with size whereas its area increases as the square.) Then Williams and Angell (1973) proposed the use of shift-registers, scanning in the tests a bit at a time, and scanning out the response a bit at a time, to reduce the need for I/O pins to a few. Eichelberger (1977) provided a complete package for such design, named *level sensitive scan design* LSSD. It simplifies both test-generation and verification (Chapter 6). It does, however, carry the disadvantage of up to 20 percent extra hardware which may make it unacceptable for very high density logic (cf. Section 4.5).

5.3.   Testing Regular Designs. It will be recalled (Section 4.4) that regular design is an interconnection of regular modules. These consist of acyclic logic preceded and followed by registers gated at different clock times, with feedback lines flowing through these registers. (LSSD is regular design plus the shift-register.) R-design has the advantage that the logic is completely determinate: there are no races or hazards an no extra hardware is required.

We have seen that in the case of a logic design which is *acyclic*, the *D*-algorithm (Chapter 3) can always compute a test to detect a failure therein. For *arbitrary* logic designs, in general with feedback, there are no known methods for such sequential test-generation, despite extensive efforts to generate them. Practical logic designs abound in feedback and so it becomes important to examine extensions of testing methods to include circuits with memory. We give such a scheme of the *D*-algorithm for *regular designs*.

In addition we shall describe methods to deal with functional decompositions by adjoining shift-registers to fractionate the design and reduce computing time for testing.

It seemed to me (1970), after extensive efforts, that an effective procedure was beyond development in the case of arbitrarily interconnected logic designs. The principal difficulty was that an arbitrary input sequence would give rise to an indeterminate output sequence. The method of regular design was defined to ensure determinate behavior, getting around one fundamental difficulty. It is easy to see (1977) that the *R*-design behavior is determinate provided one does not apply races to the registers.

The next step is to cut all of the register-to-register connections in the *R*-design, defining for each cut a pseudo-input SI and a pseudo-output SO. Call the result T*, Fig. 5.2b. No cuts with the registers are made so that in general T* is cyclic. Suppose then it is desired to compute a test of length *p*. Then *p* copies of T* are connected iteratively, through identification of the SOs of one with the SIs of the next. This produces the *iterated cut model* T# as shown in Fig. 5.3. Each stage *i* has its own PIs and POs, PI*i* and PO*i*, as well as input- and output-registers.

We now compute a test in T#, constituting inputs for the primary inputs PI1,...,PI*p*. This test can then clearly be treated as a *sequence*, of length *p*, of tests to the original design *R*. By construction this sequence will be devoid of indeterminacies (races, hazards).

To extend the *D*-algorithm to the iterated cut model T#, we must compute *D*-cube sequences and singular cube sequences for the register; since the registers are cyclic, sequences of inputs are in general necessary to define their behavior.

In Fig. 5.4 is shown a simple 1-bit register, from which all registers in a design may be constructed. Below it is a partial listing of *D*-cube and *C*-cube (singular cube) sequences. This listing is sufficient to construct a complete list. Unlike the case for acyclic blocks, to set up the desired condition in a cyclic register it may be necessary to initiate certain conditions in previous time frames.

First it is necessary to compute the D-cube sequences necessary to drive a D-chain through the register. In the absence of failures, in order to insert a 0 on the output y, Fig. 5.4, we impose the input pattern $c=d=0$. This value is held with the input $c=0$, $d=1$. To produce a 1 on y the input $c=d=1$ is followed by the same hold pattern.

For the D-chain impinging upon d from some other part of the design, the necessary D-chain sequence consists of the single D-cube

$$
\begin{array}{ccc}
c & d & y \\
1 & D & D
\end{array}
\quad \text{or} \quad
\begin{array}{ccc}
c & d & y \\
1 & \overline{D} & \overline{D}
\end{array}
$$

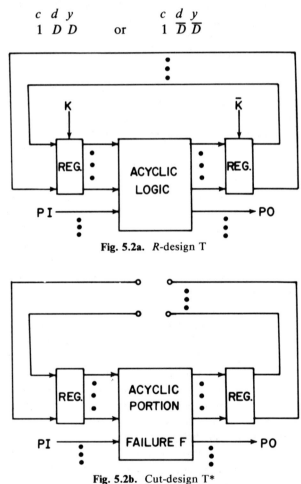

Fig. 5.2a. R-design T

Fig. 5.2b. Cut-design T*

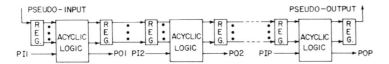

Fig. 5.3. Iterated cut model T#.

By a similar computation, one finds the *pdc*-sequence for input *d* to be

$$
\begin{array}{ccc}
c & d & y \\
0 & 0 & 0 \\
0 & 1 & 0 \\
D & 1 & D
\end{array}
$$

Both of these sequences would also serve as *pdcf*-sequences for failures stuck-at-one (s-a-1) or stuck-at-zero (s-a-0), originating within the input lines themselves.

Now we compute the *pdcf*-sequences for each of the blocks in the register. First consider line *e* s-a-0. Here $00\overline{D}$, on lines c,d,y becomes a *pdcf* (primitive-*D*-cube-of-failure). On the other hand for *e* s-a-1, an actual sequence is necessary: 000, 010, 11*D*.

Exercise. Compute the *pdcf*-sequences for s-a-1 and for s-a-0 for blocks *f*, *g* and *y*.

For failures originating in the registers it is necessary to compute the *pdcf* sequences to start out the *D*-algorithm. This may be done by analysis of the state tables or by simulation. We assume that this has been done.

A failure in the original *R*-design, whether in the registers or in the acyclic portions, will appear as *p* failures, one for each stage, in the iterated cut model T#. Because of this complication the *D*-algorithm DALG has to be modified slightly to take this, effectively, multiple failure into account. Basically, failing lines are allowed to assume only values consistent with their "stuck" value. If a given line fails by

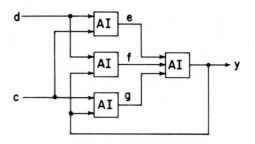

TABLE

D–CUBE SEQUENCES FOR FAILURES

FAILURE	TEST INPUT
	c d e f g y
e s–a–0	00D11D
e s–a–1	00　　0
	01　　0
	11　　D
f s–a–0	001D1$\overline{D}$
f s–a–1	11　　1
	01　　1
	01　　D
g s–a–0	0011DD
g s–a–1	11　　1
	01　　1
	10　　D
y s–a–0	110xx D
y s–a–0	00111$\overline{D}$
d pdc	00　　0
	01　　0
	D1　$\overline{D}$
c pdc	1D　$\overline{D}$

Fig. 5.4. 1-bit register and its *pdcf*s and *pdc*s (partial list)

being stuck at 0, then in all stages of T# it is allowed values only of 0 or *D*.

In going through a register, whether in *D*-drive or in CONSIST-ENCY, it is in general necessary to go to the registers immediately preceding it, to apply the appropriate "*D*-sequence" or "*C*-sequence".

As a practical tool the regular design method plus the DALG extension relieves one of the need for the insertion of shift-registers in loops, *a la* LSSD, to render cyclic designs acyclic for test purposes (1977). This additional hardware reduces effective area. It also exacerbates layout and wiring. For high volume products this may be a crucial consideration. The price one pays for DALG extended to *R*-design is much more computation.

A *second scheme* for alleviating the computational testing for *R*-design is shown in Fig. 5.5. Essentially a complete (and large) design is split functionally, preferably at a high level such as PL/R (1973), into a number of regular designs R1, R2,... . Shift-registers (1973) are inserted at the interfaces of these R*i*. They achieve the effect of isolating the Rs for purposes of test-generation, applying to each the extended DALG as outlined above. This substantially reduces the cost of the test computations at the expense of a few additional shift registers.

5.4.   Regular TESTDETECT. In the generation of tests-for-failures, it is usually desired to have an assemblage *A* of tests *T* which will detect any of a prescribed category *C* of failures *F*. Thus it is appropriate to have an algorithm which will compute a test to detect some selected failure. It is also mandatory, in the process of generating *A*, to be able to ascertain all failures of *C* detected by test *T*. One way is simulation. TESTDETECT is faster. In Chapter 3, TESTDETECT was described for the acyclic case; that description therefore is valid for LSSD designs.

In this section we extend TESTDETECT to the case of regular designs wherein, in general, a test-for-failure consists of a sequence of PI-patterns. Because of the construction of regular designs, all such tests will be determinate.

We shall describe the extension (1972) by means of an example. In Fig. 5.6a and 5.6b is shown a regular design composed of AIs only. For simplicity registers are not shown. With no loss of generality, because of the use of segmentation (Chapter 2), the design has only

one output.   One would perform TESTDETECT once for each output
PO.   The test consists of the following PI sequence:

$$1110$$
$$1010$$

In Fig. 5.6a the first pattern is applied to PIs 1,2,3,4 respectively, to
determine the resulting signal on each line (block) of the circuit; the
value for a block is shown within the block; if, because of the un-

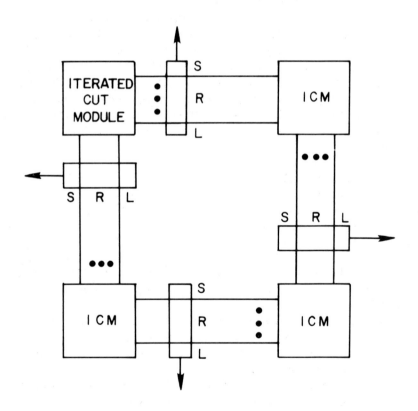

SRL = SHIFT – REGISTER LATCH

Fig. 5.5 Second scheme

known signals on the feedback loops, the signal on a given line is undetermined, this line is assigned the symbol x.

Then the TESTDETECT process of calculation is begun at the primary output and proceeds similarly to the acyclic algorithm.

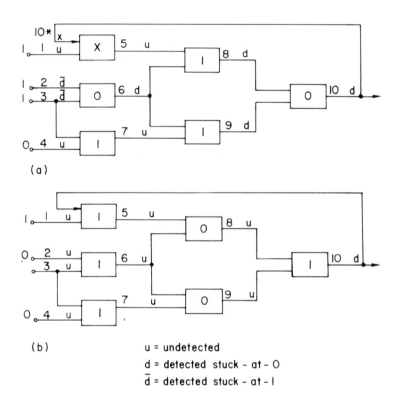

(a)

(b)

u = undetected
d = detected stuck - at - 0
d̄ = detected stuck - at - 1

Fig. 5.6. Sequential TESTDETECT, example.

The essential difference shows up in the computation of signals on each line caused by the PI pattern and the unknown x values on the feedback loops (registers): it is a 3-valued logic rather than 2-valued. E.g., if the inputs to a 2-input AI are 1 and x, then the output will not be predictable, so that it will be assigned the symbol x.

The possibility that the signal assigned to a line might be x also complicates the backwards computation. Clearly if a line has an x on it, then it is not tested by the test pattern.

Starting with the PO, we see that line 10 has the value 0 assigned to it by the first test pattern 1110 on PIs 1,2,3,4. Therefore line 10 is tested for the failure stuck-at-1. We now proceed backwards. Line 9 has the signal 1 on it and the other input, line 8, has the value 1. It follows that line 9 is tested for stuck-at-0: a D emanating from 9 would pass through block 10 to reach the PO. Similarly, line 8 is tested for the failure stuck-at-0.

Consider now line 7, feeding block 9. The other input 6 feeding 9 is 0 under the first input pattern, so that 9 will have the value 1, regardless of that of 7. Hence 7 is untested by this input pattern: we assign to it in the figure the symbol u, to denote *untested*.

In similar fashion one shows 6 untested. Line 5 is untested for the prior reason that the input pattern, together with the unknown state 10*, does not define a signal on 5: it has the value x. Primary inputs 1,2,3,4 are untested because their successors are untested. They are thereby assigned the value u.

Let us consider the second pattern 1010 with the signal 0 on the feedback, in Fig. 5.6.b. This pattern yields the signals 111001 on lines 5 through 10. By similar analysis, we see that only 10 is tested. In this fashion TESTDETECT is generalized for the case of regular designs (cf. 1973, Roth).

5.5   Delay Testing. There is a delay in response to inputs for all logic circuits. In R-design or in LSSD the "cycle time", time between waves of input patterns, is constructed to account for average delays of the primitives. Suppose that the delay of one individual circuit in the acyclic portion is substantially increased. How to detect such a delay failure? We extend the D-algorithm for this purpose in the following way.

Suppose it is desired to test a given circuit for being slow in switching say from a 0 to a 1. We select a first pattern assigning a 0 on the offending circuit. Then a D is assigned to this circuit for the second timeframe and the D-algorithm is invoked to develop a D-chain impinging on a PO, the pattern determined in terms of PIs. The direction of D-drive will be determined by the longest, next longest, etc., path open for choice as determined by a delay calculator. Similarly for CONSISTENCY. The optimized D-algorithm may also be applied to the delay-testing problem.

5.6. Short Testing. Suppose that two lines in a logic circuit touch and become (unintendedly) a "Dot-Or", i.e. an Or induced by the contact. (In some technologies we could have instead a "Dot-And.") function.

Exercise: Detect that this is the case, i.e. find input patterns to a Dot-Or whose output differs depending upon whether or not the short occurs.

In the event that no new feedback is introduced, as shown in 1966, no difficulties are encountered in extending the D-algorithm. If the "dotting" of the two wires introduces new feedback then, because it will no longer, in general, be a regular design, it will not in general be testable. Therefore, in the D-algorithm employed at the IBM T. J. Watson Research Center, if a short introduces new feedback it is declared to be untestable.

Exercise. Define the D-algorithm to cover acyclic shorts.

5.7. Other Work. It is perhaps surprising that many manufacturers compute their tests for chips by hand, even Western Electric in Massachusetts (while simulating these tests by computer). In our process it was possible to use manually or previously generated tests, to cut down on run time and handle different cases, these tests frequently utilizing the originator's understanding of design; in some cases, notably for error tolerant ALUs, it was extremely beneficial. Perhaps a combination of manual and automatic is best.

A large number of manufacturers, including some located in Japan and the USSR, have systems operating for test generation. In particular Bell Telephone Laboratories has the LAMP System (Menon and Chappell, 1978). IBM in particular uses TESTDETECT.

Suppose that manufacturer A designs and fabricates a computer, say a microprocessor, (largely) from LSI modules made by manufacturer B who does not supply the logic diagrams, gives only "functional specifications"? How does A generate tests for failures? Manufacturer A selects a "gold" module, one which is thought to be correct; he uses a shift register with feedback (1967, Golomb; 1977, Frohwerk;

1972, Peterson and Weldon), easily to generate many input patterns to the module. The responses of the gold module are recorded; these inputs and responses are then fed to other copies of the module; 100% failure coverage cannot be guaranteed but, in this way a high coverage can be achieved.

If the module, having say 50,000 circuits, contains a computer then programs can be written for the computer to check itself and the remainder of the module.

The D-algorithm has been used for logic verification (Chapter 6) and for regular-algorithm verification (Chapter 9) in the case where the two designs or algorithms are almost the same - as e.g. exists for engineering changes. In each case effectiveness soars.

Problems

5.1. Define an algorithm for the loop-cutting procedure (using if you wish the R-notation).

5.2. Apply your algorithm of problem 5.1 to the example of Fig. 5.1.

5.3. Make a block diagram or other means of description of a logic design using LSSD.

5.4. Estimate the percentage of extra hardware required for a logic design to be regular.

5.5. Assuming regular design compute a test for line 6 stuck at 1 in Fig. 5.6. For line 8. For line 10.

5.6. Apply TESTDETECT to each test in 5.5.

5.7 Apply TESTDETECT in Fig. 5.6 the patterns 1,1,1,1 followed by 0,0,0,0.

5.8. Define a calculus for the symbols 0,1,x,u, FD of TESTDETECT.

Bibliography

1966. Roth, J. Paul, "Diagnosis of Automata Failures: A Calculus and a Method," *IBM Journal of Research and Development*, vol. 10, pp. 278-291.

1967. Golomb, Solomon W., "Shift Register Sequences," *Holden-Day, Inc.*, San Francisco, CA.

1970. Roth, J. Paul, "On a Method of Design to Facilitate Testing", IBM T. J. Watson Research Center, Yorktown Heights, NY 10598, RC 2853.

1971. Putzolu, Gianfranco R. and J. Paul Roth, "A Heuristic Algorithm for the Testing of Asynchronous Circuits," *IEEE Transactions on Computers,*, vol. C-20, pp. 639-647.

1972. Roth, J. P., "Conception d'Ordinateurs Diagnostible", (Design of Diagnosible Computers), Colloque International Conception et Maintenance des Automatismes Logiques, Toulouse, France.

1972. Peterson, W. Wesley and E. J. Weldon Jr., "Error-Correcting Codes," *The MIT Press*, Cambridge, Massachusetts, cf. pp. 192, 3.

1973. Roth, J. P. "Cyclic TESTDETECT", *IBM Technical Disclosure Bulletin* vol. 15, pp. 146-148.

1973. Williams, M. J. Y. and J. B. Angell, "Enhancing Testability of Large Scale Integrated Circuits via Test Points and Additional Logic," *IEEE Transactions on Computers*, vol. C-22, pp. 46-60.

1974. Halliwell, H. and J. P. Roth, "System for Computer Design," *IBM Technical Disclosure Bulletin*, vol. 17, pp. 1517-1519.

1974. Chang, H. Y., G. W. Smith, R. B. Walford, "LAMP: System Description", *Bell Systems Technical Journal*, vol. 53, pp. 1431-1449.

1977. Roth, J. Paul, "Hardware Verification," *IEEE Transactions on Computers*, vol. C-26, pp. 1292-1294.

1977.   Eichelberger, E. B. and T. W. Williams, "A Logic Design Structure for LSI Testability," *Proceedings 14th Annual Design Automation Conference*, sponsored by ACM and IEEE, IEEE Catalog Number 77 CH1216-IC, New Orleans, pp. 462-468, New Orleans, June.

1977.   Frohwerk, Robert A., "Signature Analysis: A New Digital Field Service Method," *Hewlett-Packard Journal*, vol. 28, pp. 2-8.

1978.   Roth, J. Paul, "Sequential Test Generation", *IBM Technical Disclosure Bulletin*, vol. 20, pp. 3332-3336.

1978.   Menon, P. R. and S. G. Chappell, "Deductive Fault Simulation with Functional Blocks", *IEEE Transactions on Computers*, vol. C-27, pp. 689-695.

Chapter 6

LOGIC VERIFICATION

Introduction. In a contemporary technology built on LSI or VLSI (very large scale integration), changes, modifications, in a computer chip design are expensive, difficult and time-consuming, especially engineering changes in the field after the product is shipped. There is considerable motivation therefore to assure that the design is correct before fabrication.

A working, practical verification system has been achieved. To determine whether a design is correct it is clearly necessary to have some *other* specification of the function to be performed by the design. For a design of any significant complexity, a behavioral description, consisting of corresponding PI- and PO-sequences, is usually not possible because of the combinatorics involved. We assume this "other" specification to be in the form of another design or high-level PL/R specification thereof. The behavioral description of a parity circuit of n inputs, for example, would require $2**n$ input/output pairs for its complete specification. A parity design itself, on the other hand, would require no more than $2*n$ 2-input Xors. Thus a design can be much more combinatorially frugal than its behavioral specification.

In Section 6.1, verification between two acyclic designs is treated, using VERIFY, a modified subroutine of the D-algorithm. Sections 6.2 and 6.3 extend VERIFY to LSSD and regular designs. Section 6.4

considers verification of a logic design against algorithmic specifications, an important case, for which VERIFY and RTRAN have been used. Section 6.5 treats the case of verification between two incompletely specified designs. Finally Section 6.6 treats the case of verification between almost equivalent designs; for this important case, arising for example from engineering changes of a design, the D-algorithm is adapted for verification purposes, resulting in an order of magnitude increase in speed over VERIFY. In addition, for this case, there will be a correspondence between feedback variables which will further simplify computations.

6.1. Acyclic Verification. Assume hardware designs A and B, both acyclic. Assume between A and B a one-to-one correspondence between primary inputs PIs and primary outputs POs. Are A and B equivalent? Expressed negatively, does there exist a PI pattern for which the PO patterns of A and B differ? Using the algorithm VERIFY, we establish equivalence or else generate counter-examples to their equivalence.

Again and throughout this chapter, by the segmentation trick (Chapter 2), it may be assumed with no loss of generality that each design has a single binary primary output PO. Segmenting drastically reduces running time for verifying.

We then join designs A and B by identifying, according to their assumed one-to-one correspondence, their PIs. We start the attempted construction of counter-examples by assigning *opposite* (binary) outputs to their POs. At each stage, all implications possible by further assignments are made; for example if a line, say a PO, has assigned the value 0 and it is an AI, then it is implied that each input to this AI has the value 1.

The *C-frontier* consists of all unassigned variables (lines) which are inputs to variables already assigned and whose values have not been justified by one or more of their inputs. VERIFY makes next a choice of element in the C-frontier, e.g. on basis of nearness to PIs, and takes all possible implications thereof. At each decision-point it also keeps track of all alternate choices remaining: the status of the alternate choices remaining is stored. Each such choice defines a new C-frontier.

If a new choice causes a contradiction with previous choices and their implications, then VERIFY backs up and makes a new choice at the last decision-point. VERIFY continues in this recursive fashion until either the primary inputs are reached and no C-frontier remains (the PI pattern with possibly some xs determining a counterexample), or else the C-frontier disappears and no counterexample has been generated, in which case the designs are equivalent.

For arbitrary acyclic designs, the running time of VERIFY grows exponentially with complexity of the design although segmentation substantially reduces it.   For control logic, however, it tends to grow more nearly *linearly* with size.

A proof of the validity of VERIFY may be based upon the validity proof (1966) of the D-algorithm upon which it is based: VERIFY is a specialization of the CONSISTENCY portion of the D-algorithm.

Exercise. Write a direct proof of VERIFY.

VERIFY Example.   Consider the operation of VERIFY in a small example in Fig. 6.1.   Here we are given designs A and B, with common primary inputs $a, b, ..., h$ and (single) outputs q and r respectively.   All

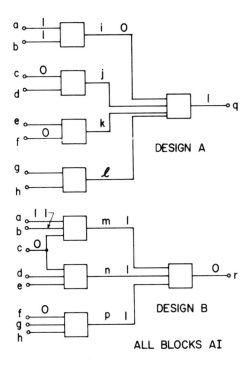

Fig. 6.1 VERIFY on a small example

logic blocks are AIs. The algorithm starts by assigning to q and r the opposite values 1 and 0. Since r is an AI with value 0 assigned, it follows that all of its inputs m,n,p must be 1. To justify the 1 on line (block) q it is necessary that (at least) one of its inputs must be 0. Choose, lexicographically, i to be 0. Reaching back in the C-frontier, for i to be 0, its inputs a,b must all be 1. Now a and b are PIs for design B as well. But with primary inputs a and b equal to 1, for block m to be maintained at 1 it is necessary that input c be 0. This assignment simultaneously satisfies the condition that n be 1. The only remaining assignment from the C-frontier is that p be 1. This can be achieved by giving PI f the value 0, with no inconsistencies anywhere.

This gives us the PI pattern

$abcdefgh$
110xx0xx

Here the values x, for d, e, g, h indicate that these PIs may be arbitrarily assigned and a test-condition holds. This is the counter-example: the same input pattern yields conflicting output patterns.

Next we look at verification of LSSD designs.

6.2. Verification of LSSD Designs. Essentially LSSD reduces a cyclic design to an acyclic one for test purposes. For verification, it renders each register accessible. States become pseudo-inputs and pseudo-outputs. To compare LSSD designs F and G it is convenient to define equivalence in the following way: between F and G we assume a one-to-one correspondence not only between PIs and POs but also between pseudo-inputs SIs and pseudo-outputs SOs (inputs and outputs introduced by cutting feedback loops). The values of the SIs and SOs will be termed the *state* and *next-state* respectively (cf. Fig. 5.2). Then we say that F and G are *inequivalent* if there exists a PI-pattern and a state SI such that the resulting PO-pattern *or* next-state pattern SO differ. They are *equivalent* if no such patterns exist.

Thus by treating states as pseudo-inputs etc. and requiring a much stronger pairing than the classical definitions (1968), LSSD verification is reduced to the acyclic case. This results in an enormous simplification in the complexity of computation; LSSD furthermore represents a method of construction of some modern computers.

In Section 6.4 we determine equivalence between high-level specifications, e.g. in PL/R, and a detailed implementation through the use of RTRAN and VERIFY together.

6.3.   Regular Verification.   Regular design (Chapter 4) requires less hardware than LSSD and its test mode is usually simpler.   Because of the added hardware and of packaging considerations the speed of an LSSD design could be less.   We will show that it is unnecessary to have LSSD to verify cyclic sequential logic.   Regular logic can be verified, at the price of considerably more running time.

Verification Procedure.   Assume we are given regular designs R and S, with a one-to-one correspondence between PIs, POs and registers.   In R and in S, all feedback loops between paired registers are cut, to form cut designs CR and CS.   No correspondence between registers of R and S are assumed.   The registers themselves are untouched, so that CR and CS contain feedback in their registers.   Suppose it is desired to compute a test of length p to distinguish R and S.   Then copies p of CR are interconnected by linking the pseudo-outputs of each copy (ith) with the pseudo-inputs of its successor copy (($i+1$)st), $i=1,...,p$-1.   This yields an iterated cut design ICR (cf. Chapter 5).   It has a set of primary inputs PIi and primary outputs POi, one for each iteration in ICR.   There are pseudo-primary inputs, going into the first stage and pseudo-primary outputs leaving the last stage which cannot be used: no values other than x may be assigned.   In exactly similar fashion the iterated cut design ICS is formed.   Suppose then we desire a sequence of length p so that we deal with two iterated cut designs ICR and ICS of p stages.   One selects a corresponding pair of primary outputs in stage p and segments the designs accordingly.   A segment with respect to a set of primary outputs consists of all the logic feeding one of the set of POs and only that logic.   For purposes of verification (or test-generation) it is sufficient to deal with segments.   It effects substantial reductions in computation time for verifying (and testing).   Then the process of VERIFY is adapted to the segmented ICR and ICS, to generate sequences of input patterns of length p distinguishing the two designs R and S.   By regular design these sequences are determinate.

The essential additional task is to drive back through the registers: the cube sequences for the registers are dependent upon the implementation of the registers.   For the hazard-free latch (Chapter 5), the cube sequence applying the set value 1 is 111;0x1.   For applying the set value 0, it is 100;0x0.   The first cube of the sequence would be applied at the register immediately preceding the register in question.

Experience with an APL system for sequential test generation would indicate that a sequence of length three usually suffices to detect a distinction between two small regular designs if one exists. To establish equivalence, however, requires for n registers in general looking at sequences of length $2**n$. To bring verification costs to reasonable levels the method for large systems, as shown in Fig. 5.5, may be used. Here a small amount of hardware substantially reduces computations.

6.4. Verification Against Algorithmic Specifications. Suppose that we have a high-level formal specification S for the logic of a computer. It might be in the form of flow-charts, incorporated into a flow-chart language. The language PL/R described in Chapter 4 above would be an instance of such a language (not a flow chart language). Suppose further that this design is subjected to intensive simulation so that this high-level specification is thought to be reliable. Suppose that a logic implementation L is performed by designers following the specification S.

Problem: decide whether S and L are equivalent; if inequivalent, produce counter-examples, i.e., input/output sequences distinguishing them. This validation problem is solved as follows.

1. A design A is automatically produced from S by compiler RTRAN (described in Chapter 4). It is assumed that L and A are both regular designs or both LSSD designs.
2. Apply VERIFY, either in its regular or LSSD mode as appropriate, to determine the equivalence of L and A, producing counter-examples if such exist.
3. Since RTRAN produces a faithful implementation A from S, S and L are equivalent if and only if A and L are equivalent.

Fig. 6.2 depicts the method of verifying a high-level specification against a detailed logic design; this form has been used (1978).

6.5 Consistency of Incomplete Designs. Given two high-level specifications of two logic designs in PL/R, one can ascertain their equivalence by transforming them into logic by RTRAN and then determining equivalence of these realizations with VERIFY.

In the logical design process, however, it is common that the logic at any stage of completion is not completely defined. Furthermore there may be natural DON'T-CARE conditions. In this section we extend the definition of PL/R so that it may be used to define incompletely specified algorithms; the compiler RTRAN is extended to

HARDWARE VERIFICATION

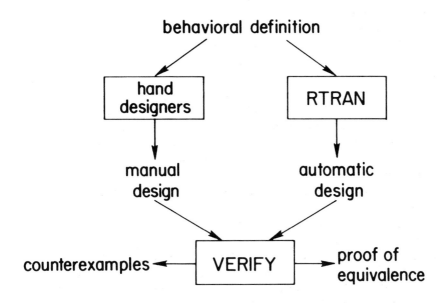

Fig. 6.2. Verification of high-level specification
against detailed logic

realize these incomplete designs in correspondingly incomplete hardware; the algorithm VERIFY is extended so as to determine the consistency/inconsistency of these incomplete designs. These three developments serve to define a process for determining the consistency of two incompletely specified algorithms.

We shall consider a simple incompletely specified design. Let a and b be (input) variables and z an output variable. Then we may have the expressions *if* $a=1$ & $b=1$ *then* $z=$F; *if* $a=0$ & $b=0$ *then* $z=$G.

There are two conditions whose outcomes U are unspecified, namely for $a=1$ & $b=0$ and $a=0$ & $b=1$; we express these total conditions, specified and unspecified, by the table

a	b	z
1	1	F
0	0	G
0	1	U
1	0	U

where U is used to denote an unspecified state: $z=$U means that z has an undetermined value.

We then extend RTRAN to produce a kind of logic realization according to these conditions, Fig. 6.3.

In the construction of high-level, abstract designs for computer hardware it is generally the case that these constructions are logically incomplete: values of some outputs are as yet unspecified for some values of inputs. Yet it is highly desirable at early stages of design to assay their correctness: more precisely to ascertain their *consistency vis a vis* some other design, also in general incompletely specified.

The above verification techniques enable one to compare effectively two designs *completely specified* whether defined at a high- (PL/R) or low- (RLD) level; these techniques have been used within IBM.

In order to adapt these methods to incomplete algorithms, we make the following extensions. First we extend PL/R so that it includes the possibility of allowing for incomplete specification - essentially by the use of the unspecified value U. Second we extend the definition of VERIFY so that a counter-example to the equivalence of two extended PL/R algorithms is automatically restricted to lie in the CARE conditions for each (incomplete) design.

PL/R extension. PL/R may be considered to be a very small subset of PL/I or, for that matter, of APL or any major language containing, in addition to the logical operations &, $|$, $\neg$, the *DO*, the *if-then-else* (written in logical form), together with the ability to utilize macros (Chapter 4). The logical functions of PL/R, the DO and the method of macro formation, remain the same in the extension for incompleteness. The only instruction added is the *if-then*. As illustrated in the example treated in Fig. 6.3, an *if-then* statement is given by a *condition* in terms of the values of some of the variables of the design followed by a consequent specification of values of other variables; e.g. *if $a=1$ and $b=1$ then $z=$F*, where z is a design variable and F is the output of a macro.

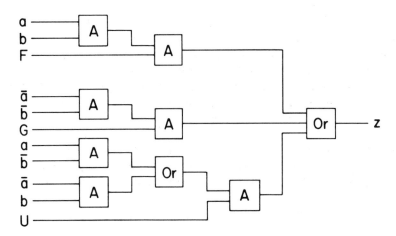

Fig. 6.3. Realization for incomplete specification

Here, however, the set of common conditions, i.e. shared input variables, need not as in PL/R be exhaustive. The *compiler* RTRAN (Chapter 4), also extended, will compute a cover (Chapter 1) for the residue input variable combinations and will assign to each cube in such cover, values U, for each corresponding output.

RTRAN Extension. Fig. 6.3 is a prototype of means for implementing PL/R extended to allow for unspecification. The only change in RTRAN is the inclusion for incompletely specified *if-then* conditions in the PL/R: the remainder of the compiler is unchanged. For each related set of *if-then* conditions (in the simplest version, related by the designer) extended RTRAN will compute a cover, as stated above, for the unspecified conditions, i.e., it will adjoin, in the first stage, a set of cubes of the type

$$(a1 = v1,...,ak = vk) \mid (y1 = U,...,yl = U);$$

where: $a1,...,ak$ are input-condition variables; $v1,...,vk$ are their corresponding values of 0, 1 or x (Chapter 1); $y1,...,yl$, their output-condition variables and U, the symbol indicating their unspecification for these values of the as.

RTRAN would in its *raw* logic (Chapter 4) implement, as illustrated in Fig. 6.3, in the first two levels an And for each set of input conditions, ANDed with the corresponding output conditions, the output of each such condition ORed together with a similar configuration for the unspecified cover ANDed with the symbol U. RTRAN will then translate, as in the present program, this raw logic into AI-, N-logic, for convenience of verification.

VERIFY Extension. The extended VERIFY algorithm will operate as previously except for its treatment of the unspecification symbol U. For purposes of illustration let us consider another incomplete design as in Fig. 6.4.

The PL/R (extended) description for the second design is

> *if* $a=0$ & $b=0$ *then* $z=$J
> *if* $a=0$ & $b=1$ *then* $z=$K

(all other conditions unspecified). Fig. 6.4 shows an extended RTRAN implementation.

Applying extended VERIFY, we start by assigning opposite values to their primary outputs - seeking conflicts - and reasoning backwards in the logic, seeking to find primary input patterns consistent with these conflicts.

We see that input pattern $a=0$, $b=0$ yields for the first design the value G whereas for the second, J: these may be in conflict depending upon their subsequent values.

If a U is encountered in any line of reasoning it is abandoned as if conflicting results were obtained.

In the classical VERIFY, values of 0 or 1 are iteratively assigned to certain variables, lines in the logic; in extended VERIFY, some lines are *a priori* given the value U (for "unspecified").

6.6 Consistency Between Almost Equivalent Designs. Frequently an engineering change is made to a design and the question is whether or not the changes have made some untoward modifications. Specifically suppose that a change is made to the manual design but that an isomorphism of function has previously been established between most of

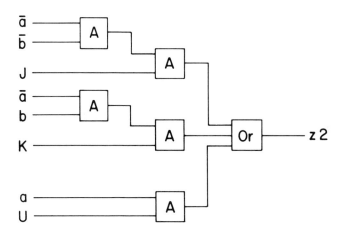

Fig. 6.4. Implementation of second incomplete design

the manual and automatic design (Section 6.4). What is wanted is to ascertain whether the modification is consistent with the automatic design. It turns out that the D-algorithm (Chapters 3,5) may be used for this purpose, very substantially reducing running time as compared with VERIFY. The method will be illustrated in Fig. 6.5. Here we have primary inputs a through h, internal lines i through r and primary output s; all blocks are assumed to be AIs. Assume that an engineering change caused line k to be disconnected from block p, no other change being made. Then the computation for the *pdcf* is made:

$$
\begin{array}{ccc}
k & l & p \\
1 & 1 & 0 \\
0 & x & 1 \\
x & 0 & 1
\end{array}
\quad \text{good circuit}
$$

$$
\begin{array}{ccc}
x & 1 & 0 \\
x & 0 & 1
\end{array}
\quad \text{changed circuit}
$$

$$
\begin{array}{ccc}
0 & 1 & D \\
1 & 0 & D
\end{array}
\quad \textit{pdcf}
$$

yielding *pdcf*s $01D$ and $10D$ on lines k,l,p; let $01D$ be the starting point of our computation. The D-frontier consists solely of r and the single *pdc* to penetrate r is $1\overline{D}\overline{D}$ on lines n,p,r, whose D-interface with $01D$ on lines k,l,p is $011D\overline{D}$ on lines k,l,n,p,r (no decisions are necessary). Likewise its D-interface with $1\overline{D}D$ on lines q,r,s yields $011D1\overline{D}D$ on lines k,l,n,p,q,r,s Next CONSISTENCY is formed to complete the test cube

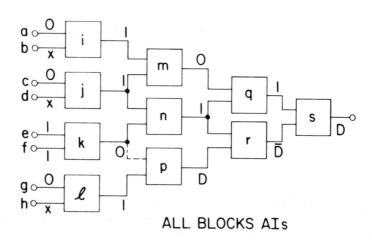

ALL BLOCKS AIs

Fig. 6.5 Verification of almost equivalent designs using the
D-algorithm

$a\ b\ c\ d\ e\ f\ g\ h\ i\ j\ kl\ mn\ p\ q\ r\ s$
$0\ x\ 0\ x\ 1\ 1\ 0\ x\ 1\ 1\ 0\ 1\ 0\ 1\ D1\ \overline{D}\ D.$

This computation yields eight tests distinguishing the two designs. VERIFY for this circuit is a much lengthier computation (cf. Problem 6.1 below); it has several levels of decision and is much longer. In fact in general the DALG computation for this important special case is an order of magnitude faster. Furthermore in general in nearly equivalent designs there will be a one-to-one correspondence between feedback variables, allowing these to be verified, and avoiding the necessity of iterated tests. These two facts greatly increase speed. Further, almost-equivalence is a common case

6.7. Other Work. Extensive use of simulation for verification purposes has been used, even though only exhaustive simulation is equivalent to verification; simulation raises one's confidence as to correctness but never in general confirms it.

The $P*$ technique described in Chapter 2 may be used to generate the set of all input patterns distinguishing two acyclic logic designs. One simply assigns differing signals on each corresponding primary output pattern and performs $P*$ on this array. The running time and storage requirements would very much exceed those of VERIFY.

Using the D-algorithm for the case of almost equivalent (or almost identical) designs is used to affect in Chapter 9 for regular algorithm verification.

Problems

6.1. Compute a test for the engineering change of Fig. 6.5 by use of VERIFY.

6.2. Assume a similar disconnection of line a and compute a distinguishing test by the D-algorithm.

6.3. Make a comparison of speeds of VERIFY and the D-algorithm for almost equivalent designs.

Bibliography

1966.   Roth, J. Paul, "Diagnosis of Automata Failures: A Calculus and a Method", *IBM Journal of Research and Development*, vol. 10, pp. 278-291.

1968.   Hennie, Frederick C., "Finite-State Models for Sequential Machines", *John Wiley & Company*, N. Y.

1973.   Roth, J. P., "VERIFY: An Algorithm to Verify a Computer Design", *IBM Technical Disclosure Bulletin*, vol. 15, pp. 2646-2648.

1973.   Roth, J. P., "VERIFY MACHINE", *IBM Technical Disclosure Bulletin*, vol. 16, pp. 856-8.

1974.   Roth, J. P., "Regular-Algorithm Verifier", *IBM Technical Disclosure Bulletin*, vol. 17, p. 1242f.

1975.   Roth, J. Paul, "Generation and Verification of Hardware Designs at a High Level", IBM Thomas J. Watson Research Center, Yorktown Heights, NY   10598, RC 5779.

1977.   Eichelberger, E. B. and T. W. Williams, "A Logic Design Structure for LSI Testability", *Proceedings of the fourteenth annual Design Automation Conference under joint sponsorship of the ACM and IEEE*, New Orleans, IEEE Catalog No. 77 CH1216-11.

1978.   Roth, J. Paul, "Hardware Verification", *IEEE Transactions on Computers*, vol. C-26, pp. 1292-1294.

Chapter 7

LOGIC EMBEDDING

Introduction. After the logic is designed in the LSI or VLSI process it is necessary to map the graph of the design into a "chip" or set of chips. In this context a chip will be defined as a set of rectangular solids connected together as determined by the technology. A "cell complex" is introduced, a generalization of the cubical calculus of Chapter 1, to keep track of the connections that are made in the embedding process, mapping the logical design into a physical design. A premise of this approach is that any procedure must proceed one step at a time, and it is therefore necessary to keep track of the totality of paths that remain available (as well as the totality of paths that are unavailable). The "cell calculus" defined in this chapter admits such a process.

First an appropriate cell calculus is introduced, in which to describe the "space" of paths available at any one time (step) of the embedding algorithm: it is a generalization of the cubical calculus introduced in Chapter 1. The cell calculus includes the adapted operations of *interface*, the *#-product* and an *embedding* algorithm, which was programmed and run. Paths in this calculus are chains of cells; chains are designed to interconnect vertices or cells; after a chain connecting two vertices is constructed, a linear path between them, contained entirely within the chain, connects the vertices. The selected path is then subtracted ("sharped") from the original space, etc.

7.1.   Cell Calculus.   A *cell* consists of two triples of non-negative integers, $<(a1,a2,a3)(A1,A2,A3)>$, the first triple $(a1,a2,a3)$ being coordinates of the vertex closest to the origin $(0,0,0)$, the second $(A1,A2,A3)$ being the point furthest from the origin.   The *dimension* is the number of coordinates i for which $ai<Ai$.   Thus $<(0,0,0)(3,4,0)>$ has dimension 2 while $<(1,2,3)(1,2,3)>$ has dimension 0.   For example $<(0,0,0)(4,1,0)>$ defines the two-dimensional cell, called a *2-cell*, in Fig. 7.1 below.

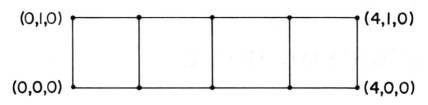

Fig. 7.1. 2-cell $<(0,0,0)(4,1,0)>$

Cell $c=<(c1,c2,c)(C1,C2,C3)>$ is   a   *face*   of   cell $d=<(d1,d2,d3)(D1,D2,D3)>$ if $di \leq ci \leq Ci \leq Di$, $i=1,2,3$.   We shall also say, under this condition, that d *contains* c.   The above arithmetic embodies the intuitive geometrical relationship.

A set K of cells is a *cell complex* or, simply, *complex* if whenever it contains a cell of K then it contains all faces thereof.   It will be termed *Boolean* if, in addition, whenever it contains the *vertices*, the 0-dimensional cells, of a cell, then it contains the cell itself.   In general, all complexes will be Boolean.

Let COV be a set of cells, to be called a *cover*.   COV is said to *cover* a set of cells E if every 1-dimensional and 0-dimensional face of the cells of E is contained in some cell of COV.   In embedding a graph into a cell complex we shall use, at each stage of the iterative process, covers of the available as well as covers of the unavailable paths.

7.2.   Interface. The *interface* of cells c and d consists of the largest cell determined by the vertices, 0-cells, they have in common.   Let $c = <(c1,c2,c3)(C1,C2,C3)>$ and $d = <(d1,d2,d3)(D1,D2,D3)>$.   If for any coordinate i, $Di < ci$ or $Ci < di$, then the cells are said to be *disjoint* - they have no vertices in common.   The empty cell is denoted ϕ.   If c and d are not disjoint then the *interface* is defined as:

$$<(\max(c1,d1),\max(c2,d2),\max(c3,d3)),(\min(C1,D1),\min(C2,D2),$$
$$\min((C3,D3))>$$

where max denotes the maximum of its two arguments and min, the minimum.   The interface of cells c and d is denoted $c \ I \ d$.   In Fig. 7.2 examples of interfaces are sketched.   For simplicity, only two dimensions are used.

7.3.   #-product. Given cells c and d, their #-product $c\#d$ consists of a cover of all cells of c that do not belong to d.   In a sense it is the complement of the interface.   Before we give a formal definition let us consider an example.

In Figure 7.2, a and c are disjoint and so $a\#c = a$.   Consider $c\#d$. Here d completely envelops c so that $c\#d$ is empty.   On the other hand $d\#c$ consists of four overlapping rectangles surrounding c, as we shall see from the definition of #.

Given arbitrary cubes u and v, $u\#v$ will be defined with respect to the universe of u, using the interface of u and v.   In 3 dimensions for $a = <(a1,a2,a3)(A1,A2,A3)>$ and $b = <(b1,b2,b3)(B1,B2,B3)>$, in the nondegenerate case, wherein b is a subcell of a, $a\#b$ consists of six cells:

$$<(a1,a2,a3)(b1-1,A2,A3)>, <(B1+1,a2,a3)(A1,A2,A3)>,$$
$$<(a1,a2,a3)(A1,b2-1,A3)>, <(a1,B2+1,a3)(A1,A2,A3)>,$$
$$<(a1,a2,a3)(A1,A2,b3-1)>, <(a1,a2,B3+1)(A1,A2,A3)>.$$

Exercise. Define the #-product for the degenerate case, that is, where one or more coordinates of a and b are equal.

The   #-product   applies   to   sets   of   cells.   If $d = <(d1,d2,d3),(D1,D2,D3)>$ is a cell and C is a set of cells, $C = C1,C2,...,Ck$, then $d\#C = (...(d\#C1)\#C2)\#...)\#Ck$.   Similarly if D is a set of cells $D = D1,D2,...,Dm$ then $D\#C$ is defined as the cover formed by $D1\#C,...,Dm\#C$.   In actual practice, however, we have found it expedient to perform the CONTAIN operation on each cell: if, in a cover, e contains f then f may be removed from the cover, for e contains all the information that f has.

In general an algorithm for interconnection will select a path connecting two vertices. If K is represented by a cover C and p denotes a path to be removed, one performs $C\#p$ to keep track of the remaining "space" of available paths.   Algorithms for embedding utilizing the cell calculus were programmed by Hamed A. Ellozy (1975). These were successfully applied to several chips.   The option of performing CONTAIN at every #-operation was found to be highly beneficial; in one example a running time of 280 seconds was reduced to 0.5 seconds by this technique.

A further reduction in running time was achieved by removing redundant cells from the cover at each stage of the computation.   Cell

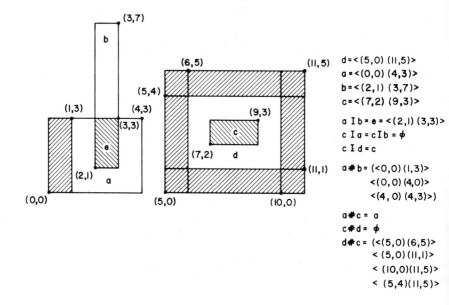

Fig. 7.2. Geometric representation of cells,
their interfaces, and their #-products

u in cover C is *redundant* if $u\#(C-u)=\phi$. It is sometimes preferable, in performing a number of #-operations, to perform this removal function only when the number of cells exceeds a certain bound, so that removal is justified. Given a cell complex K, a *component P* is a subspace of cubes having the property that, between any two vertices of P there is a path lying entirely within P and there is no superset of P having this quality. Interconnection can take place only within components.

A cell is *prime* if no cell containing it lies entirely within complex K. One can use the double #-method for generating the prime cells, as for cubical complexes. If the cover defining the component consists of all its prime cells then it is easy to determine connecting paths and redundant cells.

7.4 Embedding Algorithms. A program was written for interconnection (embedding). Instead of, as in Lee's algorithm (1961), having to search through all vertices, labelling their distance from one cell until reaching the second cell of the interconnection, here one deals with cells and finds chains of cells interconnecting two vertices. Having such a connecting chain it is simple to construct a path therefrom. Fig. 7.3 shows a chain of cells connecting points p and q; a *path* between p and q is shown, constructed therefrom: the figure illustrates how a path is deduced from a chain of cells. This considerably improves the execution time for the search procedure over vertex schemes, by almost an order of magnitude.

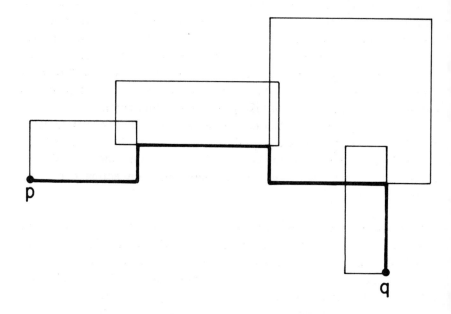

Fig. 7.3. Deduction of path from chain

7.5   Other Work.   An interesting class of initial placement techniques, developed by Kurtzberg (1965), are the *pair-linking method* and
the *cluster development method*.   In these algorithms, the placement
configuration is generated by sequentially selecting unplaced modules
and adjoining them to a subset of already placed modules that com-
prise the partially formed configuration.   Once modules are positioned
they are not moved.   The final configuration can be accepted as the
design placement or in turn can be operated upon by a placement
improvement technique.

The particular rules for selection (or ordering) and positioning of
the modules define the specific methods.   In the pair-linking method,
the unplaced module which has the highest connectivity to any module
already placed is selected.   It is then positioned as close as possible to
that module.   The implications of each choice for selection and positioning are taken into account to resolve any ties.

In the cluster development method, a measure of the expected
number of interconnections to the set of placed modules for each
unplaced module is computed and the one with the highest value is
chosen.   It is then positioned in the weighted center-of-gravity of those
modules already placed to which it must be connected.

These methods have the twin virtues of requiring a comparatively small amount of computation time (the order of growth for both methods is $n**2$, where n is the number of modules) and yet are sufficiently good for many practical applications even without need for any subsequent iterative placement improvement technique.

Problems.

7.1. Form the #-product

$$<(2,0)(6,2)>\#<(4,0)(5,8)>$$

Verify your result with a sketch.

7.2. Form the interface I of the cells of problem 7.1.

7.3. Prove that

$$a\#b = a\#(aIb).$$

Bibliography

1961. Lee, C. Y., "An Algorithm for Path Connections and Its Applications", *IRE Transactions on Electronic Computers*, vol. EC-10, pp. 346-365.

1965. Kurtzberg, J. M., "Algorithms for Backplane Formation", *Microelectronics in Large Systems, Spartan Books*, pp. 51-76.

1974. Roth, J. P., "Regular Embedding", *IBM Technical Disclosure Bulletin*, vol. 17, pp. 1257-1261.

1975. Ellozy, H. A. and J. P. Roth, "Large-scale Integration Physical Design Procedures", *IBM Technical Disclosure Bulletin*, vol. 17, pp. 2465f.

1975. Ellozy, H. A., "Path Connection Methodology for LSI Circuits", *IBM Technical Disclosure Bulletin*, vol. 18, pp. 1262-1265.

Chapter 8

REPAIRABLE LOGIC

Introduction. Computers sometimes fail. For correct behavior the failures must be eradicated in their functioning. One traditional technique has been manual detection followed by diagnosis followed by replacement. For micro-miniature technologies (e.g. Josephson technology, 1977) this procedure is very difficult to apply. The problems of detection and diagnosis are exacerbated as evidenced by the test procedures of Acyclic Testing and Sequential Testing in Chapters 3 and 5. The problem of replacement is also compounded because of the "minusculeness" and relative inaccessibility of the failing parts: e.g., imagine a microminiature chip immersed in a liquid helium bath. Exotic procedures seem required for repair purposes.

The *universal function schema*, defined in this chapter, is a design schema which permits automatic detection, diagnosis and repair of failing logic within a chip, module or board. By its means, any computer design can be realized, up to physical limitations. The price is multiplication of the required hardware by an order of magnitude.

First we build a universal And, UA, and a universal Or, UOr. Then we construct all logic from these universals. It is equally feasible to use AIs (or Nors). The trick is to have 1-bit memory devices, in the form of shift-registers, each controlling one variable, in the sense that the input to a given UA or UOr can be allowed to "pass through" or to be blocked. These are connected to form any computer. The design may be modified, hence repaired, by a change in the "connection vector", the contents of the shift-register.

In this chapter, first a schema is described for a universal element, capable of realizing any function, up to the allowable number of circuits subject to fan-in and fan-out restrictions and other limitations. Second it is shown how to interconnect these, again with physical limitations, to form a universal functional schema UFS, capable of realizing any computer design. Such a universal computer is capable not only of behavior modification; it also has the ability to replace failing elements by general purpose spares. This repair ability can be used in manufacture, increasing chip yields, but also in the field, where automatic repair can be used to extend the life and functioning of the machine.

This work was supported in part by the Jet Propulsion Laboratory, California Institute of Technology, under the National Aeronautics and Space Administration Contract NAS-7-100.

8.1. Universal Element. The universal element is addressed to the problem of the proliferation of the number of parts - cards, chips - necessary for conventional implementation in an LSI technology of computer systems - terminals or peripheral systems. This schema would use only one or a few parts, the various specializations being effected by insertion of appropriate connection vectors.

To utilize this universal functional schema implementation, the designer would proceed in the conventional manner, either manually or with compilation of the logic from a high-level hardware language (Chapter 4), to produce a "simplex" design SD. A simple program then faithfully translates SD, having no redundancy, into a universal design. Experience to date indicates that the universal design requires about 10 times as many circuits as a conventional implementation, independently of the size of the design. There will be only one - maybe a few - distinct chips formed so that manufacturing, stocking, and costs for engineering changes should be reduced. Consider that a failure in a universal-schema has occurred. By current practice the entire chip, card or module would have to be replaced. With the universal schema we have means to disconnect the failing circuitry and replace it using a universal spare by a new connection vector. This procedure can also be used in manufacture and for effecting engineering changes.

8.2.   Two-level universal function schemas. First we shall consider the special case of the 2-level UFS. The general case will then be near at hand. We first devise a universal A of r inputs. Each input variable ai, $i=1$ to r, to the And will appear, and its negation $\overline{ai}$ as well. In the normal A of r inputs we would have simply an And box, with r input lines feeding it. Instead, for the universal A denoted UA, each input variable ai will feed a 2-input Or, whose other input is a 1-bit memory device mi. Now if $mi=1$, then the input from the ai variable will be masked: the input to the UA from the ith Or block Ori will be 1, so that it will not determine the output from the UA. But if $mi=0$, then the input ai will feed effectively directly into the And. See Fig. 8.1. In similar fashion we have ai's negation $\overline{ai}$ feeding the And through the medium of an Or driven by $\overline{ai}$ and another single-bit memory device ni. When ni is 0, $\overline{ai}$ feeds the And. When ni is 1, the ai is turned off from effect over the And.

Then if we want ai effectively to feed the And we set $mi=0$ and $ni=1$. If $\overline{ai}$ is desired, then set $mi=1$ and $ni=0$. If we wish neither ai nor $\overline{ai}$ to affect the And then both controls mi and ni are set to 1. Then the $2*r$ memory devices, mi and ni and r Ors, together can effect each of the $3**r$ And functions, varying according to their primary input variables.

See Fig. 8.1 wherein the 1-bit registers are represented by circles. It is seen that a UA is a kind of *selection device* selecting any one (or more) of r signals or their negations.

Exercise: Devise a universal And using AIs.

8.3.   Functions realized by UAs. The 2-input Exclusive-or Xor is shown on the left of Fig. 8.2. The ON-array for the Xor consists of the two singular cubes for input variables a,b and output e, respectively, 01 | 1;10 | 1. We need therefore, in our Xor fabrication, two UAs, each with the four inputs $a,\overline{a},b,\overline{b}$, as shown. Here the cube $a\&\overline{b}$ is realized on the left by four Ors driven by controlled inputs $a,\overline{a},b,\overline{b}$ and driving an A. The cube $\overline{a}$ and b is realized on the right by four Ors driving an A. The output of each A feeds a controlled Or which in turn feeds a final Or. This Or would in general have outputs from other UAs as inputs which could be used as *spares* in case the original circuits fail. Suppose that a failure has been detected and diagnosed. In this event, the appropriate connection vector switches out the failing member and switches in an appropriately personalized spare. The *connection vector* is the sequence of values of the control variables in shift-register form. Note that the final Or, plus its input apparatus, constitutes a universal Or, UOr.

CIRCLES DENOTE
CONTROL REGISTERS

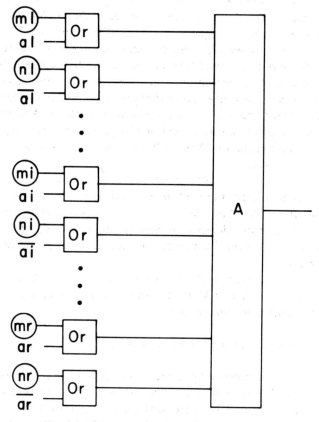

Fig. 8.1 Universal And UA, with r inputs

8.4   Universal AI. An And-Invert AI is an And whose output is inverted.   Any function can be realized by an AI.   The design of a universal AI could also be done with Ands and Ors but, because of its universality, a simplicity of presentation with AIs is possible.   Consider an AI with inputs $a1,...,ar$ and possibly their negations $\overline{a1},...,\overline{ar}$, Fig. 8.3.   Each ai and $\overline{ai}$ feeds a 2-input AI whose other input will be from a single-bit memory device - denoted by a circle - mi and ni.   All blocks are AIs, of two or more input variables.

If it is desired that aj (j=1 to r) feed the AI, then its accompanying memory input mj will be set to 1.   For in this case, the output of the 2-input AI would be $\overline{aj}$.   On the other hand if it is desired that aj

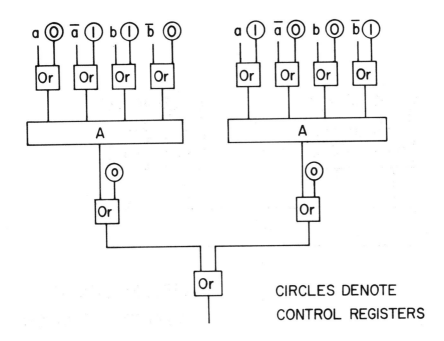

Fig. 8.2. UFS XOr

not feed the AI then *mj* is set to 0, making the input to the large AI constantly 1, regardless of the value of *aj*. With *mj*=1, *aj* is turned on.

Similarly memory control *nj* causes $\overline{aj}$ to feed the big AI when *nj*=1 and to be noneffective when *nj*=0. If *mj*=*nj*=0 then both *aj* and $\overline{aj}$ are turned off. (Similarly for *mj*=*nj*=1). Thus any AI function of *r* variables can be so realized.

A similar arrangement can be made to determine a function realized by several levels of logic, Fig. 8.4; here the control memory elements are assumed but not shown. At the first level of logic stand all the outputs *b1*,...,*bs* and their negations $\overline{b1}$,...,$\overline{bs}$ from the first level, for potential input to the second level of logic. If a primary-input variable, *ai* or $\overline{ai}$, is to feed a second level of logic then it feeds through a first-level AI, itself being the only input.

Each level of logic has memory controls on its arguments and its negations.

Suppose that some input variable *ai* becomes stuck in value; then this variable will be switched out, by setting *mi*=*ni*=0, and it will be

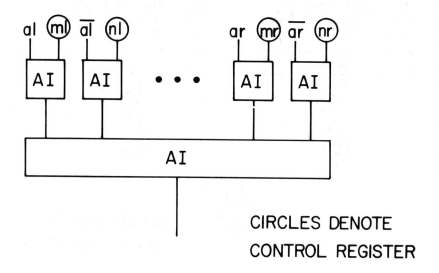

CIRCLES DENOTE
CONTROL REGISTER

Fig. 8.3. Universal AI, UAI

necessary that another AI, having ai and $\overline{ai}$ as inputs, be switched into place.

Suppose now we consider an extension to more levels. Call the outputs from the first stage of universal AIs, $b1,...,bs$. For each bj, $j=1,...,s$, there will be generated their negations, $\overline{b1},...,\overline{bs}$ and these, the bjs and $\overline{bj}$s, will be available for next level implementations. Some of the bs will act as universal *spares* for subsequent processing. Let variables of level 1 be $a1,...,ar$; level two, $b1,...,bs$;...; level z, $z1,...,zt$. Then denoting the universal AI as UAI we have Fig. 8.4 as the diagram for z-level logic. Each level will have spares for replacements.

On each level there will be a number of UAIs, some to be used as spares for replacement of failing elements. Not elements ¬ allow the formation of the negations of the UAI outputs.

Then the second level of logic is constructed in fashion similar to the first, with outputs c_j and their negations, and similarly for as many levels as is allowed by the technology, in particular, by the timing.

8.5   Feedback. With physical limitations of size and number and because of sequentiality, it is necessary in the universal schema to introduce feedback (1978).   It will be assumed that the design is regular as defined in Chapter 4. Suppose then we have a universal-schema design for the acyclic portion of a regular logic design, as in

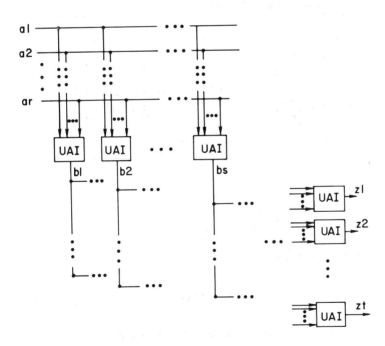

Fig. 8.4.   Multiple level universal circuit

Fig. 8.5. Suppose that lines $t1,...,tk$ enter an output register (not shown in Fig. 8.5) in the simplex design being implemented.

Let there be input variables $s1,...,sk$ with which the t may be connected; either by the control mechanism ti becomes an input to the universal function circuit at this level, or else si becomes a primary input, $i=1,...,k$. Because of the repair aspect, there will be spare feedback lines, with each of these spares able to perform any of the $t1,...,tk$ (not shown in Fig. 8.5). Likewise the primary outputs from the module will have spares which can be accommodated to any of the POs (also not shown).

The registers on the input side will have spares. From level to level there will be varying numbers of feedback loops. The method of

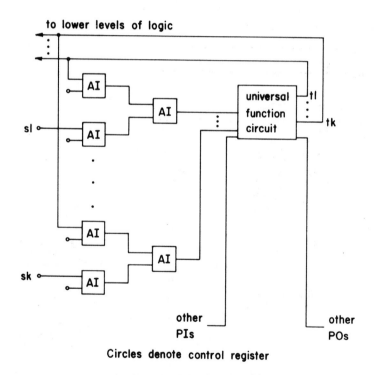

Circles denote control register

Fig. 8.5. Universal regular module handling feedback

accommodating the input lines to the control register is as shown in Fig. 8.5.

The output signals, in this first schema, are fed by either of two output loops through the medium of the "steering device", which determines which of the two, or either, will be in the feedback loop: if both control signals in the steering device are turned off then a constant signal of 1 will be delivered to the input register.

Each register, input or output, may accept as many inputs as the technology affords in fan-in. The portion within the acyclic universal circuit is constructed as in previous sections and is subject to repair through change of the connection vector which is the contents of the shift-register chain which forms the control.

8.6   Other Work. The architecture, organization and operation of an automatically repairing computer ARC was described in 1967. The design includes storage, "read-only-store" and arithmetic/logical elements which were all failure-tolerant. Means were given for automatically detecting and replacing failing elements; necessary designs for reconfiguration switches, status registers and fully checked decoders were given. These techniques required 2.5 times more hardware than a "simplex" computer. A 600-fold increase in component failure rates would be required to obtain the same increase in reliability in a simplex computer. The key technique of ARC was the incorporation, for each critical portion of the design, of (specialized) *spares* for replacement of failed modules; the control therefor was efficiently arranged in cyclic fashion.

Earlier work (1962, 1966) studied "the design of digital circuits to eliminate catastrophic failures", a failure in which if it is not (logically) eliminated, the design will drastically malfunction. The underlying technology was the cryogenic-superconducting wires immersed in liquid helium, unsuccessful predecessor of Josephson technology. A method of organization was developed in which catastrophically failing elements would be replaced automatically by "standby" spares. The "replacement system splits a simplex machine into a number of parts; each part is supplanted by a package consisting of several replicas of the part it supplants; if one part of the original machine is connected to another, then interconnecting circuitry and control circuitry is provided which enables any one of the replicas of the first to be connected to any one of the second" (1962). Reliability calculations were performed on various configurations. For (near) optimum configurations, substantial increases in reliability over the original machine were obtained, but an order of magnitude below that of the individual circuit, unlike the studies of von Neuman (1956) and Moore and Shannon (1956) for more benign technologies.

Problems.

8.1.   Construct a 2-bit adder from UAIs.

8.2.   Construct a 2-bit adder from UOrs, UAs and UIs (universal inverts).

8.3   Make a study of the reliability of the universal function schema, specifically for your designs in problems 8.1 and 8.2.

1956. von Neumann, J., "Probabilistic Logics and the Synthesis of Reliable Organisms from Unreliable Components", Automata Studies, Annals of Mathematics Studies No. 34, pp. 43-98. *Princeton University Press*, Princeton, NJ.

1956. Moore, E. F. and Shannon, C. E., "Reliable Circuits Using Less Reliable Relays", *Journal of the Franklin Institute*, vol. 262, pp. 191-208, 281-297.

1961. Roth, J. Paul, "Lectures on the Design of Automata", Lectures Notes of the Special Summer Session on Logic, Switching Systems and Automata, *Moore School of Electrical Engineering, University of Pennsylvania*, Philadelphia, PA.

1962. Griesmer, James H., Raymond E. Miller, J. Paul Roth, "The Design of Digital Circuits toEliminate Catastrophic Failures", Proceedings of a *Symposium on Redundancy Techniques for Computing Systems*, sponsored by the ONR and Westinghouse, Spartan Books, Washington, DC.

1966. Roth, John Paul, James H. Griesmer, Raymond E. Miller, John L. Selfridge and Eric G. Wagner, "Serially Connected Logic Stages with Means for Bypassing a Selected Stage", United States Patent, No. 3,235,842.

1967. Roth, J. P., W. G. Bouricius, W. C. Carter, and P. R. Schneider, "Phase II of an Architectural Study for a Self-repairing Computer," IBM T. J. Watson Research Center, Yorktown Heights, N. Y. 10598. U.S. Air Force Space and Missile Systems Organization, Air Force Systems Command, Los Angeles, CA. SAMSO TR-67-106, DDC accession no. AD825-460.

1974. Roth, J. P., "Repairable Large-Scale Integrated Logic Unit", *IBM Technical Disclosure Bulletin* vol. 17, pp. 1226-1228.

1974. Roth, J. P., "Universal Chip", *IBM Technical Disclosure Bulletin*, vol. 17, pp. 1234-1236.

1974. Roth, J. P., "Omniwafer", *IBM Technical Disclosure Bulletin* vol. 17, pp. 1245-1246.

1977. Anacker, W., "Josephson Functions as Computer Elements," *Inst. Phys. Conf. Serv.* No. 32.

1978. Roth, J. P., "Universal Logic Schema", *IBM Technical Disclosure Bulletin*, vol. 20, pp. 4216-4217.

Chapter 9

R-ALGORITHM VERIFICATION

Introduction. We have been concerned in this book primarily with *algorithms*, e.g., defined by the *R*-notation (Chapter 1), as contrasted with *programs*, which have a distinctive one-instruction-at-a-time format, and which are designed for the von Neumann computer structure. In this chapter we extend *R*-notation to incomplete *R*-algorithms; convert (incomplete) regular algorithms into (incomplete) logical realizations; transform the question of *consistency* of *R*-algorithms into the corresponding problem of the consistency of their (incomplete) logical realizations; and use the hardware verification techniques of Chapter 6 to decide their consistency, up to a bounded number of iterations. Verification is the purpose of these hardware realizations. In particular, if the two algorithms are almost equivalent, a common special case, e.g. *versions*, then the *D*-algorithm may be used introducing an order-of-magnitude increase in speed over VERIFY. The verification of programs is a much more difficult proposition (King, 1979; Anderson, 1979; 1978). One basic difficulty with programs is in explicitly representing the functions that they compute considering the fact that the computers on which they run execute only one instruction at a time. The *R*-algorithm which, like hardware, admits multiple parallel execution, lends itself to easy translation into hardware where the logic verification procedures of Chapter 6 can be applied.

First the extended *R*-notation is defined including the arithmetic primitives in addition to those of PL/R. The new primitives - for fixed size arguments - are then converted to logic by RTRAN. Each *R*-algorithm if it is recursive must include a *bound b* for the number of iterations allowed: the hardware realization of the algorithm provides only for *b* iterations. Verification, more precisely the *consistency* between *R*-algorithms, is defined for these bounded models. Verification is effected (Section 9.4) with VERIFY for various cases, with the *D*-algorithm for greater speed, in the common case where the *R*-algorithms are almost equivalent. It is estimated that the *D*-algorithm will verify *R*-algorithms whose hardware realizations do not exceed 50,000 blocks.

9.1 *R*-**Notation for Incomplete Regular Algorithms.** Our first task is to define a notation for the specification of algorithms that are incomplete, as in general they are during their initial design; the notation is extended from the cubical calculus and its generalization in *R*-notation (Chapter 1). According to vanCleemput, 1979, it bears similarities to the programming languages ALGOL and PASCAL.

Variables & Implications. We begin with *variables, u, v, ..., w*, which can take on *values a, b, ..., c* , which with no loss of generality are assumed to be strings, called *cubes*, of symbols 0, 1, x, of fixed length.

The *assignment* to variables $u1,...,ur$ of values $a1,...,ar$ respectively is expressed as

$$(u1=a1)...(ur=ar);$$

Assignments are *consistent* if they have no common variables with conflicting values. An *implication* between assignments $(u1=a1)...(ur=ar)$ and assignments $(v1=b1)...(vs=bs)$ is written

$$(u1=a1)...(ur=ar) \Rightarrow (v1=b1),...,(vs=bs);$$

and has the meaning: *if* $u1=a1$ *and* $...ur=ar$, *then* $v1=b1$ *and* $...vs=bs$. Such an implication is termed a *cell*. $(u1=a1)...(ur=ar)$ and $(v1=b1)...(vs=bs)$ are termed the *input-* and *output-assignments* of the cell. *Cells* are *consistent* if whenever the input assignments are consistent then so too are their output assignments.

A consistent set of cells is termed a *cell-cover* or simply *cover*, which defines a *primitive function*.

Box-nodes of a Cover. For purposes of simplification we shall restrict ourselves to "single-output" cells. Any cell cover can so be decomposed. Given a cover C, consisting of a consistent ensemble of cells, consider all cells having a common output variable v. We shall draw a common box, i.e. node, with output v, with the variables for each of these cells as inputs, and with each of the individual cells written within the *box-node*.

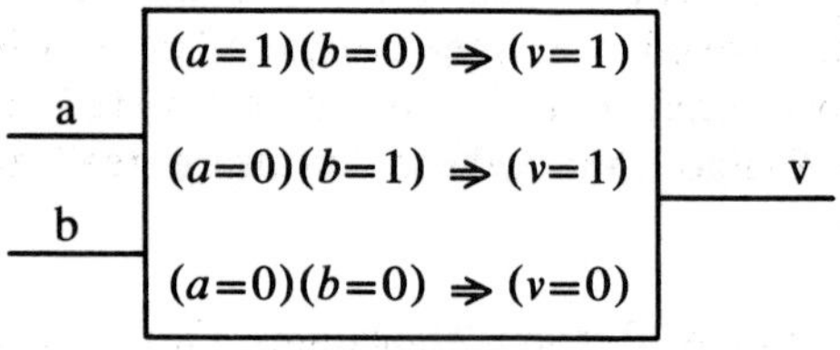

$$
\begin{array}{l}
(a=1)(b=0) \;\Rightarrow\; (v=1) \\[4pt]
(a=0)(b=1) \;\Rightarrow\; (v=1) \\[4pt]
(a=0)(b=0) \;\Rightarrow\; (v=0)
\end{array}
$$

Fig. 9.1 Example of box-node for output variable v of a cell-cover

The box-nodes of a cell-cover define a *graph* G of the cover C, by identification of outputs of box-nodes with identically labelled inputs of box-nodes of another; if an output variable is identified with several variables, the graph allows *fan-in* or *fan-out* to accommodate it in the graph G. Input variables of box-nodes of G which are *not* identified as output variables of other box-nodes are termed *primary input variables*, denoted *pi*. Output variables not identified in G as input variables of other box-nodes are termed *primary output variables*; in addition various output variables of the cover may be made by *fiat* primary output variables. Let the primary output variables be denoted *po*.

In the case when G is *acyclic*, then C defines, by composition, a function F of *pi*s into *po*s. Combinational (acyclic) logic circuits are special, *completely specified*, cases. In general the function F is not complete in that its response to any member of the cartesian product of its *pi*s is not always defined. (In fact, in general, each box-node will have its own DON'T-CARE conditions).

Let B be a box-node, u its input- and v its output-variables; let the function so defined be written

$$v = B(u);$$

Consider an acyclic graph G defined as above by "I/O" identifications of variables; let the "box-functions" defined by the nodes of G

be $v1=B1(u1)$, $v2=B2(u2)$,..., $vr=Br(ur)$, where ui and vi are the
input- and output-variables of Bi, $i=1,...,r$; let the function B defined
by G be written

$$po=B(pi);$$

then the algorithm defined by G will be expressed in the form (cf.
R-notation, Chapter 1)

$$<po=B(pi) =: v1=B1(u1); ...; vr=Br(ur)>$$

where the symbol $=:$ is to be read as "is defined by". This notation
was adopted for the expression of *R*-algorithms and will be construc-
tively defined here to have a natural constraint of *boundedness*.

An acyclic ensemble of primitive functions: $y1=F1(u1),...,yn =$
$Fn(un)$, where the ys and us are sets of variables and the Fs are covers
of implications defining functions, defines a new composite function
$y=F(u)$ of the primary input variables u of the ensemble into the
primary output variables y of the ensemble. This will be written

$$<y=F(u)=: y1=F1(u1),...,yn = Fn(un)>$$

Now F by definition is a composite function and, because it is acyclic,
also can be used to define other functions as a constituent thereof.
Thus, when no cycles are introduced, the composite functions may be
used in the definition of (other) composite functions. Furthermore it
can be used just as a variable in the definition of an implication, as
defined above.

A composite function F may use itself in its definition string: the
arguments used for this function appearing in its defining string must
be either primary inputs or variables computed earlier in the string;
such a function is said to be *recursive*. Our recursive functions will
always have a *bound b* associated with them: recursion is restricted to
at most b repetitions: this assures finite computability and the possibility of verification.

Consider the following example, the Babylonian (square-root)
algorithm (Chapter 4) $B(n,r,e,b)$. Here b specifies the bound on the
number of iterations of the procedure. This has the following definition

$$<y=B(n,r,e,b)=:s=S(n,r); \quad a=A(n,s,e); \quad (a=1)\Rightarrow(y=s);$$
$$(a=0)\Rightarrow y=B(n,s,e,b-1)>$$

We shall give a realization for $b=3$: first we write out explicitly - a step not necessary in practice - the algorithm in three stages

$$<y=B(n,r,e,,3) =: s1 = S(n,r); a1=A(n,s1,e); (a1=1) \Rightarrow (y=s1);$$
$$s2 = S(n,s1); a2 = A(n,s2,e); (a1=0)(a2=1) \Rightarrow (y=s2);$$
$$s3 = S(n,s2); a3 = A(n,s3,e); (a2=0)(a3=1) \Rightarrow (y=s3)>$$

This cover would define the graph shown in Fig. 9.2. Here in the first rendition of the algorithm a first, second and third solution $(y=s1)$, $(y=s2)$, $(y=s3)$ is computed. The selection of the final answer y is determined by the logic of the problem. There is no notion in the realization of repetition in time of the algorithm. It does, however, faithfully represent the function being computed by the algorithm. Note that the algorithm, in three iterations, may supply *no* answer.

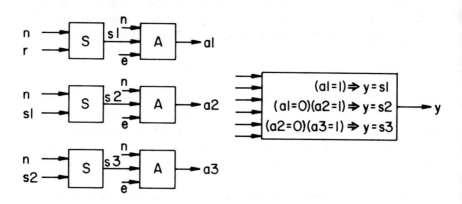

Fig. 9.2 Iterated hardware realization of Babylonian *R*-algorithm

Each recursive function employed in a string must have as its input variables previously computed variables or primary inputs.

Thus the *function* of an *R*-algorithm will be defined by a hardware compiler R which transforms it into hardware, akin to the techniques of Chapter 6; note that this definition holds for only up to *b* iterations.

9.2   Definition of Primitives.   We shall have primitives consisting of those of PL/R, And &; Or |; Not ¬; the DO function with *fixed* range; in addition we will have the arithmetic functions Sum +; Difference -; Multiply *; Divide /; the arguments and values of these functions are vectors of fixed bit lengths.

In order to endow these functions with meaning we define a transformation R, using RTRAN, to transform them into logic. Below we express Sum and Difference for 4-bit arguments in both PL/R and in their compiled state RLD.

```
=SUM(R,S,KI,T,KO);
INPUT R(4),S(4),KI;
OUTPUT T(4),KO;
DCL TX(4),TO(4),TA(4),K(4);
TX=R&¬S | ¬R&S;
TA=R&S;
TO=R | S;
K(0)=KI;
DO J=0 TO 2;
K(J+1)=K(J)&TO(J) | ¬K(J)&TA(J);
END;
T=K&¬TX | ¬K&TX;
KO=K(3);
```

and the difference

```
=DIF(R,S,BI,D,BO);
INPUT R(4),S(4),BI;
OUTPUT D(4),BO;
DCL DA(4),DX(4),B(4);
DA=R&S;
DX=R&¬S | ¬R&S;
B(0)=BI;
DO J=0 TO 2;
B(J+1)=B(J)&DX(J) | ¬R(J)&S(J);
END;
D=B&¬DX | ¬B&DX;
BO=DA(3)&B(3) | ¬R(3)&S(3);
```

The hardware implementations via RTRAN are

1R-FILE FOR SUM

R

1	2	= PI
1	3	= PI
1	4	= PI
1	5	= PI

S

1	6	= PI
1	7	= PI
1	8	= PI
1	9	= PI

KI

1	10	= PI		
1	11	= N	6	
1	12	= AI	11	2
1	13	= N	7	
1	14	= AI	13	3
1	15	= N	8	
1	16	= AI	15	4
1	17	= N	9	
1	18	= AI	17	5
1	19	= N	2	
1	20	= AI	6	19
1	21	= N	3	
1	22	= AI	7	21
1	23	= N	4	
1	24	= AI	8	23
1	25	= N	5	
1	26	= AI	9	25
1	27	= AI	20	12
1	28	= AI	22	14
1	29	= AI	24	16
1	30	= AI	26	18
1	31	= AI	6	2
1	32	= AI	7	3
1	33	= AI	8	4
1	34	= AI	9	5
1	35	= AI	11	19
1	36	= AI	13	21
1	37	= AI	15	23
1	38	= AI	17	25
1	39	= AI	35	10

1	40 = N	31	
1	41 = N	10	
1	42 = AI	40	41
1	43 = AI	42	39
1	44 = AI	36	43
1	45 = N	32	
1	46 = N	43	
1	47 = AI	45	46
1	48 = AI	47	44
1	49 = AI	37	48
1	50 = N	33	
1	51 = N	48	
1	52 = AI	50	51
1	53 = AI	52	49
1	54 = N	27	
1	55 = AI	54	10
1	56 = N	28	
1	57 = AI	56	43
1	58 = N	29	
1	59 = AI	58	48
1	60 = N	30	
1	61 = AI	60	53
1	62 = AI	27	41
1	63 = AI	28	46
1	64 = AI	29	51
1	65 = N	53	
1	66 = AI	30	65
1	67 = AI	62	55
1	68 = AI	63	57
1	69 = AI	64	59
1	70 = AI	66	61
1	71 = AI	38	53
1	72 = N	34	
1	73 = AI	72	65
1	74 = AI	73	71

T

1	75 = PO	67
1	76 = PO	68
1	77 = PO	69
1	78 = PO	70

KO

1	79 = PO	74

and for the Difference,

```
1R-FILE FOR DIF
  R
    1    2 = PI
    1    3 = PI
    1    4 = PI
    1    5 = PI
  S
    1    6 = PI
    1    7 = PI
    1    8 = PI
    1    9 = PI
  BI
    1   10 = PI
    1   11 = AI      9    5
    1   12 = N       6
    1   13 = AI     12    2
    1   14 = N       7
    1   15 = AI     14    3
    1   16 = N       8
    1   17 = AI     16    4
    1   18 = N       9
    1   19 = AI     18    5
    1   20 = N       2
    1   21 = AI      6   20
    1   22 = N       3
    1   23 = AI      7   22
    1   24 = N       4
    1   25 = AI      8   24
    1   26 = N       5
    1   27 = AI      9   26
    1   28 = AI     21   13
    1   29 = AI     23   15
    1   30 = AI     25   17
    1   31 = AI     27   19
    1   32 = AI     28   10
    1   33 = AI      6   20
    1   34 = AI     33   32
    1   35 = AI     29   34
    1   36 = AI      7   22
```

```
1   37 = AI    36   35
1   38 = AI    30   37
1   39 = AI     8   24
1   40 = AI    39   38
1   41 = N     28
1   42 = AI    41   10
1   43 = N     29
1   44 = AI    43   34
1   45 = N     30
1   46 = AI    45   37
1   47 = N     31
1   48 = AI    47   40
1   49 = N     10
1   50 = AI    28   49
1   51 = N     34
1   52 = AI    29   51
1   53 = N     37
1   54 = AI    30   53
1   55 = N     40
1   56 = AI    31   55
1   57 = AI    50   42
1   58 = AI    52   44
1   59 = AI    54   46
1   60 = AI    56   48
1   61 = N     11
1   62 = AI    40   61
1   63 = AI     9   26
1   64 = AI    63   62
D
1   65 = PO    57
1   66 = PO    58
1   67 = PO    59
1   68 = PO    60
BO
1   69 = PO    64
```

9.3   Hardware Compiler R of R-notation. On instructions that are PL/R the compiler R of R-algorithms behaves the same as the RTRAN compiler. Above we showed how to extend R to restricted arithmetic operations. Fig. 9.2 indicates how the "branch" conditions are implemented: the branch conditions, such as $(a=1) \Rightarrow (y=F(u))$; $(a=0) \Rightarrow y=G(u)$, are between *functions* not instruction numbers.

9.4   Verification of *R*-algorithms. Suppose first that we have two *R*-algorithms p,q with a one-to-one correspondence between their input variable and output variables, none between their internal variables. Suppose they are recursive and that they have the same bounds *b*. Their, in general, incomplete logical realizations P,Q are then supplied by compiler R. We may then apply VERIFY (Chapter 6), slightly generalized to accommodate incomplete specifications, to ascertain their consistency. Designs P,Q are *inconsistent* if they have a common input (CARE) condition for which their outputs are different; otherwise, *consistent*. Because of experience with its predecessor RTRAN it is expected that the running time of R is linear with complexity. On the other hand, VERIFY for hardware verification purposes has verified designs having many circuits in acceptable times.

Suppose in the second place that there is a one-to-one correspondence with the "feedback" variables; then, exactly as in Chapter 6, we may substantially reduce the computation by not having to consider iterations of the model.

Finally consider the case, as examined in Chapter 6, where the *R*-algorithms are almost equivalent or, more strongly, almost identical. Then their *difference*, i.e. the design portions that are not identical, may be treated in either of the designs as a failure and the *D*-algorithm invoked to compute a distinguishing test if such exists, reducing computation time by an order of magnitude.

Running Time. The compiler transforming regular algorithms into partial logical realizations is an extension of RTRAN (Chapter 4) and will take time almost linear with complexity. The growth of VERIFY running time is, however, exponential. In the case when the two algorithms are piecewise almost equivalent, there will in general be a one-to-one correspondence between feedback variables, enormously simplifying verification. Also in this case, the *D*-algorithm may be used. It is estimated the *D*-algorithm as defined here running on fault-diagnosis problems can handle 50,000 circuit logic designs in acceptable running times on the IBM/370 model 168. The application to algorithm verification will be simpler than to fault diagnosis in most cases because of the fact that the computation here will be required, equivalently for only one failure - the logical distinction between the two algorithms - and, furthermore, no simulation (or its equivalent, TESTDETECT) is needed. On this basis it is estimated that the *D*-algorithm will be able to verify regular algorithms whose logical realization does not exceed 50,000 blocks.

The existence and use of additional internal point correspondences can additionally drastically reduce running time; the running time using VERIFY for a 16-bit ALU was reduced by this device from several hours to 50 seconds.

9.5 Other Work. A substantial literature has been built up on the excruciatingly difficult subject of program verification (King, Anderson, 1979). These approaches require an alternate specification of a program p, in the form of mathematical "entry" and "exit" statements specifying the function to be performed by p. No general procedure, from this viewpoint, seems to be available to "prove" correctness.

Problems

9.1. Compute a test by VERIFY and the D-algorithm for line i disconnected from block m in Fig. 6.4.

9.2. Similarly for line j disconnected from n.

9.3. Attempt a logical realization of a simple *program* with a loop (cf. 1978).

Bibliography

1971. Putzolu, Gianfranco R., and J. Paul Roth, "A Heuristic Algorithm for the Testing of Asynchronous Circuits," *IEEE Transactions on Computers*, vol. C-20, pp. 639-647.

1975. Roth, J. Paul, "Generation and Verification of Hardware Designs at High Level", IBM Thomas J.Watson Research Center, Yorktown Heights, N. Y. 10598, RC 5779.

1977. Roth, J. Paul, "Hardware Verification," *IEEE Transactions on Computers,*, vol. C-26, pp. 1292-1294.

1977. Evangelisti, C. J. and J. P. Roth, "Verification of Algorithms Written in a High Level Language," *IBM Technical Disclosure Bulletin*, vol. 20, pp. 1653-1658.

1978. Evangelisti, C. J. and J. P. Roth, "Decision Procedure for Program Verification," *IBM Technical Disclosure Bulletin*, vol. 21, pp. 1310-1313.

1979. King, James C., "Program Correctness: On Inductive Assertion Methods," IBM Research Laboratory, San Jose, CA 95193, RJ 2525.

1979. vanCleemput, William. Personal communication.

1979. Anderson, Robert B., "Proving Programs Correct," *John Wiley & Sons*, N.Y.

INDEX

acyclic failure,59,60,62,68,74,
  75,82,108,112,115
acyclic logic,42,45,50,52,58-59,
  74-75,78,87-91,93,101,102,
  108,109,112-113,137,153,160
ALGOL,159
algorithm,incomplete,130-132,
  158-159
algorithm,interconnection,143
algorithms,embedding,142-143
almost equivalent algorithm,136-
  137,158,168
almost equivalent design,126,134,
  136,137
ALU,31,83,97,98,100,121,169
ALU8,97,98,100
Anacker,W.,157
And Invert AI,40,54,56,88,156
And/Or realization,8,50,101
And/Or design,51
Anderson,Robert B.,158,169,170
Angell,J.B.,92,93,106,112,124
APL,33,38,74,102,129,132
approximation,75,94-95
arithmetic,31,56,94,96,97,102,103,
  140,155,159,163,167
Arithmetic and Logic Unit,31
Armstrong,D.B.,78,82,85
assignment,2,42,61,65,109,126,128,
  159
associative logic array,31,39
automata,38,84,106,123,138,156
automatic logic,56,103,147

Babylonian algorithm,87,94,96,161,
  162
Babylonian machine,94,95
Barak,Ammon B.,57,58
Bartee,T.C.,33,38
behavioral description,89,125
Beister,J.,25,39
binary variables,40,42,97
Boole,George,2,37
Boolean difference,83,137
Boolean trees,57,105
Bottorff,P.S.,82,85
bound,2,3,4,6,11,46,57,83,96,113,
  143,158,159,161,168
bound coordinates,2,3
Bouricius,W.G.,74,84,157
branching,18,21,27,32

Breuer,Melvin A.,85,91,106,107
Brown,Albert,85,86

Carter,W.C.,84,105,107
Chang,H.Y.,85,124
Chappell,S.G.,82,85,121,124
CIMPL,103
COFACE,29
coface,4-5,7,11-12,25,33
COFF,11-16
combinatorics,89,125
compilation,92,148
compiler,33,56,87,88,96,98,99,102,
  104,105,130,133,162,167,168
complex,1,4,5,7-8,10,12-16,19-24,
  33,35,53,56,57,59,61,103,104,
  125,127-128,139-140,143,168
complexity,53,57,104,125-128,168
component,48,143,155,156
COMPOSE,51
composition,42-43,46,113,160
computational complexity,57
computer design,38,57-58,85,88,
  102,106-107,121,124-125,132,
  138,147-148,155,158
computer hardware,40,58,124,132,
  138,155,170
computer systems,84,85,88,102,103,
  107,148
compute time,29,50,82,114,125,155,
  158,169
consistency,2,4,51,130-137,158-159,
  168
CONSISTENCY,66,68,70,77,80-81,
  117,121,127,136
consistent,3,4,11,51,61,115,134,
  135,159-160,168
constrained solution,18,19,21,23
contain,2-6,8-11,13,16-20,25-26,29,
  31,50,54,64,74,81,82,87,91,96,
  102-103,109-110,122,129,132,
  139-140,142,143
CONTAIN,8,10-15,33,142
contradiction,16,80,126
control logic,56,102,127,151
Cornish,M.,105,106
cost,4,6,8,13,16,19,21,23,25,29,
  31,54,104,117,130,148
cost function,8,13,16
counter-example,48,126,128,130,132
critical faces,26,27
crown,17,35
cubical calculus,1-5,9,139,159
cubical complex,4,5,7,15,20,21,
  139,143
cubical notation,27,93,159

cuts,109,113
cycle time,120

DALG,111,115,117,137
D-algorithm,1,65-71,74-75,
    78-85,96,106,108,111,113,115,
    120-122,125-127,135-137,
    158-159,168-169
Dauber,P.S.,106
D-chain,57,61-74,77,79,81,82,84,
    114,120
D-contain,81,82
D-cube test for failure c(T,F),68,74
D-cube sequence,113-115
D-cubes,63,66,81,83
DDL,57,106
D-drive,65-68,70,75,111,117,121
decision point,80,126
decisions,32,136
degeneracy,3,4,9,141
DEL,26,28,75,93
delay,75,77,87,92-93,102,106,109,
    120-121
delay algorithm,77,93,120,121
delay path,75,93,121
delay,testing,109,120,121
delay,intrinsic,93
delay,terminal,93
DeMorgan's law
design,acyclic,44-45,50-51,56,58,
    59,68,74,89,90,92,93,101,
    108-117,125-128,137,153
design,almost equivalent,126,134,
    136,137
design,incomplete,126,131,132,135,
    159
design,physical,1,107,139,146,147
design,simplex,148,154
design,universal,147,148,150,153
detection,105,147
determinacy,87-91,94,102,112-113,
    117,129
D-frontier,64-70,73,77,80-82,136
diagnosis,1,59,84,85,92,107,108,
    112,123,138,147,168
Dietmeyer,Donald L.,57,58,106
digital design language DDL,57
dimension,5,7,14,15,23,24,26,97,
    140,141
D-interface,63-67,74,80-82,136
D-intersection,82
distinguished vertices,25,26
distinguishing algorithm,80-82,
    137,168
D-notation,61,63
D-sequence,117

Duke,K.A.,84,103
Duley,James R.,57,105,106

ECs,88,101,102
Eichelberger,E.B.,89,92,93,105,107,
    112,124
element,universal,148,157
Ellozy,Hamed A.,142
embedding,1,104,139-146
engineering changes ECs,88,101,102
equivalence,46,57,78,103,126,128,
    130,132,137
error correcting codes,124
Evangelisti,C.J.,170
exact,1,5,18,29,32,42,50,91,129,
    168
exclusive or Xor,41,46,79,89
executional statement,27,28
extraction algorithm,12,15-23,27-29,
    31-33,35,39
extraction algorithm,
    multiple-output case,23
extraction procedure,12,25,27
extremal,15-23,25-27,29,32
extremal,multiple output,25,26

face,3-16,25-27,33,48,51,63-65,
    67-68,74,80-82,117,136,
    139-142,145
factorization,51-55,57,101,103
factorization,controlled,101
failure,1,59-63,65-66,68-75,78-85,
    79,80,81,82,83,84,85,91,92,
    96,102,105,108-115,117,
    120-123,138,147-149,155,156,
    168
failure detected FD,71
failure diagnosis,1,59,84,85,92,
    123,138
failure,stuck,60,65,66,69-75,83,
    111,115,120
fan-in,2,45,48,50,51,54,59,93,102,
    103,148,155,160
fan-out,42,45,48,54,73,93,102,103,
    148,160
feedback,44,46,50,59,74,87,91,92,
    97,108,112,113,119-121,
    126-129,137,153-155,168
feedback loop,91,92,108,112,119,
    120,128,129,154-155
finite state models,138
first order extremals,16,17,19-21
Fleisher,H.,1,39
France,R.E.,85
free coordinates,2,3
Friedman,Arthur D.,85,107

Frisiani,Arrigo L.,38
Frohwerk,Robert A., 121,124
frontier,64-70,73,77,80-82,126-128,
    136
functional decomposition,113

Garges,N.H.,85
Galey,J.M.,84
geometric representation of cubical
    complex,5,15
Golomb,Solomon W.,123
goodness,53,94
graph,12,19,21,27,31,37,39,57,81-85,
    105,107,123,128,138-140,146,
    156-157,160,162,170
Griesmer,James H.,156

Halliwell,H.,33,56,58,75,96,106,124
hardware,8,40,54,58,83,87-88,94,96,
    100-103,108,112-113,123-126,
    129-132,138,147,148,155,
    158-159,162,163,167,168,170
hardware,computer,40,58,124,132,
    138,155,170
hardware design,54,87,94,96,100-103,
    108,117,126,129-132,128,138,
    168,170
hardware flowchart language,102
hardware realization,8,87,96,158,
    159,162
Hardy,Ann C.,23
hazard-free,129
hazards,92,113
Hennie,Frederick C.,138
Hewlett Packard,124
high level specification,100-102,
    109,125,128,130,131
Holtzman,Ernest,39
Hu,K.C.,58,68

IBM Journal of Research and
    Development,39,57,84,105,
    123,138
IBM Technical Disclosure Bulletin,
    39,58,85,106,107,124,138,146,
    157,170
IBM Thomas J. Watson Research
    Center,38,39,84,138,170
IBM System/360 Model 40,87,92,103
IBM System/360 Model 91,29,56,138
IBM System/360 Model 195,87,92
IBM System/370 Model 168,168
IEEE Transactions,39,57,58,84,85,
    106,123,124,138,170
implementation,faithful,130
implications,67,68,70,80-82,126,

144,159,161
inaccessibility of failing parts,
    147
inconsistencies,4,81,128
indeterminacy,87-91,94,113
inequivalence,128,130
injection operator,46
input control,104,147,149,151,154,
    155
input face,3,4,11,67
input part,2,3,13,23,52,53
input variables,2,4,5,10,13,28,
    40-43,48,50-53,65,91,97-98,
    126,131,133,134,149-150,
    154,160-162,168
interconnection,40,42,44,59,89,
    91-92,105,109,112,142-144
interface,3,4,10-12,16,33,48,51,
    63-68,74,80-82,117,136,139,
    141-145
interface of covers,4
internal variables,44,45,51,97,168
intersection,3,4,43,82,83
invert N,41,54,56,64
I/O pins,93,112
I/Os,59
IRE Transactions,38,146
iterated cut model ICM,113,115
iterative algorithm,33,111
iterative design,91,92,96,111
iterative representation,111

Japanese computer manufacturers,
    57,105,121
Jet Propulsion Laboratory,29,33,
    148
Junker,Leroy,14,29,33,39

Karnaugh,M.,37
Karnaugh map,7,37
King,James C.,158,170
Kurtzberg,Jerome M.,144,146

LAMP system,121,124
large scale integration LSI,1,102,
    125
latch,hazard-free,129
layout,78,117
Lee,C.Y.,143,146
less than LT,8,16-22,26,28,32,35,
    65,71,94,129,168
level,1,4,18,31,32,36,38,40,45-57,
    87,88,91-93,96,100-106,109,
    112,117,125,128,130-132,125,
    128,130,131,132,134,137,138,
    148-154,170

level sensitive scan design LSSD,
87,92-93,101-105,108,112,117,
120,123,125,128-130
Levy,Leon S.,58,106
Lewis,Bryan A.,39,101
lexicographical order,19,21,27,
81,82
lines,internal,44,65,66,135
logic,arithmetic,31,94,102,155
logic array,1,31,87,102
logic,control,56,102,127,151
logic design,42-46,50-57,61,63,
70,74,78,87-109,113,120,123,
126,130-131,137-139,153,155,
168
logic design,acyclic,45,50,74,93,
101,102,108,109,113,137,153
logic design,automated,38,56-57,
84-90,92,94,96,98,101-107,
121-124,130-132,138,147-148,
155-156
logic embedding,139
logic,raw,98,99,100,103,134
logic,repairable,150,154,156,157
logic,2-level,1,31,102,130
logic,universal,147,153,157
logic,3-valued,8,120
logical algorithms,32,94,96,158,
168
loop cutter,108-112
loops,56,91-92,108-111,117-120,
128-129,154-155
loops,tight,109
LSI,1,5,54,55,61,93,96,102,107,
112,121,124,125,139,146,148
LSSD,87,92,93,101,102,105,108,112,
117,120,123,125,128,129,130
LSSD designs,102,112,117,125,128,
130
LSSD testing,108,112

macros,56,60,94,98,104,105,107,
109,132
macro notation,104
macro portions of design,60
macro structure,104,105
Maissel,L.I.,39
majority MAJ,42,44,57,61,96-99,132
Manning,Eric,85
mask product,52,53
McCluskey,E.J.,37,38
memory,45,87-89,109,113,147-151
memory cells macro,109
Menon,P.R.,85,124
merging,111
Metze,Gernot,85

Miller,Raymond E.,2,156
MIN370,18,29,33,87,103
module,59,78,91,112,121,122,
144-148,154-155
module,regular,91,112,154
Montgomery,H.C.,105
Moore,E.F.,156
Muller,David E.,58
multilevel logic,101
multiple D-chain,69
multiple-output case,9,12,23,25,
26,27,33,51
multiple-output extraction
algorithm,18,23,27-29,35
Muroga,Saburo,57,58

NASA,12,29
Nelson,Raymond L.,37
Newton-Raphson algorithm,94
next state,128
non-Boolean,2,54
nondegeneracy,3,4,9,141
nonredundancy,10,11,32
Norby,R.E.,84

OFF array,12,48,57,82
OFF cover,11-16,25,34-35,46,50-51,
57
OFF cube,11-15,25,46,48,50
OFF vertices,13-16
ON array,29,48,50,52,57,82,149
ON CARE conditions,2,4,5,8,13-17,
29,36,130,160
ON complex,4,5,15,33,35
ON cover,4-17,25,29,33-34,42,
46-52,66,140,142,159
ON vertices,2,5,7,10,13-16
optimization problem,8-11
optimized D-algorithm,121
oscillations,92
output face,3,4,5,8,9,11,25-27,
67
output part,2,3,13,23,52,91
output variables,2,4,5,10,13,28,
40,45,50,51,53,97,131,134,
149,160,161,168

pair-linking method,144
parity,46,98,100,125
parity circuit,100,125
parity on 16 bits PT4,100
parity on 256 bits PT8,100
parity on 8 bits PT3,100
PASCAL,159
path,45,68,69,70,75,93,121,
139-146

pdc,61-69,75,80-83,114-116,136
pdc sequence,114-116
Perlman,M.,25,38,39
Peterson,W. Wesley,122,124
PI,39,42-51,57-60,68-75,86-92,
    99-107,113,117-120,124-129,
    157,164,166
PI and PO sequences,89,118,125
PISTAR,42,46
PL/I,18,29,30,33,56,75,88,96,97,
    98,101,104,132
PL/R,33,56,88,96-104,117,125,128,
    130,132-134,159,163,167
PL/R algorithm,33,56,96-103,132,167
PLA,1,2,88,91,102-104
PLA reduction,103
PLA system,102,103
placement,144-147,152-155
powering,102,103
predecessors,14,103,109,110,155,168
Preiss,R.J.,105
Preparata,Franco P.,57,58
primary input variable,48,50,65,
    99,149,151,160-162
primary inputs PI,42,46,50,59,89,
    92,113,126,128,129
primary output variable,45,160,161
primary outputs PO,44,59,89,92,
    126,129
prime cell,143
prime cube,5,10-19,21-27,29,33,35
prime implicant,5,38
primitive *D*-cube of failure *pdcf*,
    61,115
primitive *D*-cube *pdc*,61,63,66,83,
    115
primitive function,40,45,56,89,
    159,161,163
primitive logic,40,42,54,56,59,
    60,66,74,91,109,159
program verification,56,134,158,
    169,170
proper face,16
pseudo extremum,32
pseudo logic,56,92
pseudo inputs,91,92,101,111,128,
    129
pseudo outputs,92,101,128,129
PT2BAD,98,99,100
Putzolu,Gianfranco R.,106,123,170
P*,42,46-51,57,82-83,91,101-104,
    137

quantities,physical,40
Quine,V.W.,32,37
R-algorithm,1,28-29,33,56,83,94,

96,100-103,122,137,158-162,
    167-169

regular algorithms,158,159,168
regular logic design RLD,88,91,
    98,100
regular program,98
Reinheimer,H.J.,105
Ritz,Robert,17,37
RLD,88,91-92,98,100-103,132,163
R-notation extended,159
R*,51,102-104
Roth,J.Paul,5,12,15,25,32,33,37,38,
    39,56,57,58,70,74,77,84,85,93,
    94,96,103,105,106,107,120,
    123,124,138,146,156,157,170

stuck-at-0 sa0,60,65-66,70-75,
    83-84,115,120,123,141
stuck-at-1 sa1,69-75,84,94,111,
    115,120,123,141
scan,92,96,112
SCANIN,93
SCANOUT,93
SCD,102,103
Schneider,Peter R.,48,49,57,68,
    69,74,75,84,157
Schorr,H.,33,38
second order extremals,19-21
segment,41,46,48,50,68,71,75,117,
    126,127,129
SEL,27,29
Selfridge,John L.,156
sensitive path,68-70,75
sequence,45,75,87-91,103-104,
    111-118,123-125,129-130,149
sequence chart,103
sequence,cube,90,113-115,129
sequence,length,45,75,90-91,11-113,
    129-130
sequential diagnosis,112
sequential machine,89,138
Shannon,C.E.,2,37,156
sharp product,8-10,13-15,33-35,
    56,139-142,145
shift register,92-93,104-105,
    112-113,117,121,123,147-149,
    155
short,60,74,78,102,109,112,121,123
short failures,60,74
SHRINK,1,4,10-12,15,29,34,101-104
signature analysis,124
simulation,57,71,82,85,87,90-91,
    105-106,109,115,117,124,130,
    137,168
simulation,3-valued,90

simulation,5-valued,91
singular cover,60,89
singular cube,1,2,63,65,74,82,113,
        149
singular cube sequence,113
SLT,103
Smith,G.W.,124
space of first order extremals,25
spares,general purpose,148
specification,1,2,5,54,87,100-103,
        106,109,121,125-128,130-134,
        159,168,169
specification,algorithmic,102,126
specification,high-level,100-102,
        109,125,128-131
state,9-12,25-28,74,89,91,97-101,
        104,115,120,128,132-133,138,
        156,163,169
state tables,89,115
state variables,91,97
stuck,60,65-66,69-75,78,83-84,111,
        115,117,120,123,151
stuck failures,60,70-74,111,115
successors,64,88,109,110,120,129
system for computer design SCD,58,
        88,102,103,106,124

tape code translator,29
technology,5,29,40,45,51,54,58-61,
        93,100-103,106,112,125,139,
        147,148,153,155
test,2,48,57-87,91-96,101-137,147,
        168-170
test assemblage,59,78,85,117
test cube tc,65-68,71-74,78-83,136
test for equivalence,137
test for failure,62,65,68,70-74,78,
        80-83,91-92,105,108,111-112,
        121
test of length p,75,111,113
test condition,78,114,128
TESTDETECT,70-78,82,84,108,
        117-124,168
test generation,48,57,64,82-85,
        91-92,101-104,108,111,113,
        117,121,124,129
testing,59-86,92-93,104-129,147,170
testing,acyclic,62,64,66,70,72,
        76,78,80,82,84,86,92,108,112,
        147
testing delay,109,120,121
testing,sequential,110,112,114,
        116,118,120,122,124,147
testing,short,109,123
testpoint insertion problem,104
Texas Instruments TI,105

third order extremals,18,20
tightness,109-111
time frame,111,114,120
timing requirements,101
translator,29,57,105
truncation,32,73

UFS,148,151
universal cube,13,23
universal function schema,104,
        147-148,156
universal schema,104,147-149,153-157
USSR,121

vanCleemput,W.M.,91,105,107,159,170
vector,connection,148,149,155
Veitch,E.W.,7,37
verification,46,56,58,82-83,88,
        92,96,100-104,112,122,
        124-138,140-146,158-170
verification hardware,58,83,124,
        126,130,138,158,168,170
verification,regular,83,122,137
VERIFY,88,101-104,125-138,158-159,
        168-169
version,70,74,133,158
vertex,2,4,5,15,16,25,31,140,143
vonNeumann,J.,156,158
VLSI,93,125,139

Wagner,Eric G.,38,39,156
Walford,R.B.,124
Weinberger,1
Weldon,E.J.,122,124
Western Electric,121
Wiley,John,138
Wiley Interscience,85
Williams,M.J.Y.,106,107,124
Williams,T.W.,92,93,,106,112,124
wiring,117

Xor Exclusive Or,41,46,57,66,67,73,79,
        83,89,96,97,125,149
XT,1,7,10,17,25

#algorithm,13-15,23-25
#operation,46,142-143
#product,8-10,13-15,33-35,56,139-142,
        145
#product of covers,8,10,33,35,141

0-cube,6,8-9,15-17,29,35
0-skeleton,5
1-cube,6,29,31,34